Spel Quiz Book 1, 2, 3

Bumper Edition

John Smith

Illustrated by Clare Beaton

CASSELL

Cassell
Villiers House
41/47 Strand
London WC2N 5JE

387 Park Avenue South
New York, NY 10016-8810

Books 1, 2 and 3 first published separately 1978
This omnibus edition first published 1993

British Library Cataloguing-in-Publication Data
A catalogue record for this book is available from the British Library.

ISBN 0-304-32911-8

Printed and bound in Great Britain by Cox & Wyman Ltd, Reading

These three books are designed to give practice in spelling and to widen vocabulary.

They contain picture puzzles, questions on groups of words containing the same sound and questions on general knowledge – each page is a challenge.

The words needed to answer the questions are jumbled up in the boxes and bracketed lists at the start of each section.

The original page numbers of the three books have been retained and answers are given at the back of each book. Only correct spellings should be counted.

Spelling
Quiz Book 1

CONTENTS

a

bat	hat	rat
lad	bag	gas

1. It has four legs and a long tail   _____
2. It is used for hitting a ball   _____
3. Some Mums use this for cooking   _____
4. Another name for a boy   _____
5. This is worn on the head   _____
6. We put things in a —   _____

e

ten	peg	hen
leg	bed	pen

7. A bird   _____
8. We sleep in a —   _____
9. 10   _____
10. To hang your coat on   _____
11. We use this to write with   _____
12. A part of the body   _____

1

i

pin	hit	sit
tin	lip	bit

1. A part of the mouth   _____

2. This has a sharp point   _____

3. Some foods come in a —   _____

4. Chairs are used to — in   _____

5. A piece   _____

6. We — a nail with a hammer   _____

o { hop   cot   log   top   dog   fog }

7. A baby's bed   _____

8. A pet   _____

9. Mist   _____

10. The girl tried to — on one leg   _____

11. A piece of a tree   _____

12. The cream is on the — of the milk   _____

2

u

| fun | bull | mug | |
| nut | hug | rub | cub |

1. We can drink out of this _____
2. Throw your arms around a person _____
3. It grows on a tree _____
4. A farm animal _____
5. We do this when we polish something _____
6. A baby fox _____
7. He is always happy and full of — _____

y { why try cry dry fry

8. Not wet _____
9. '— are you upset?' asked the teacher _____
10. We — to write neatly _____
11. I like my Mum to — me an egg _____
12. Tears came into his eyes and he began to — _____

3

car	tar	bar
far	jar	star

1. For putting jam in _____

2. Play near the house, don't go — away _____

3. It twinkles in the sky _____

4. It has four wheels _____

5. Used for making roads _____

6. A metal rod _____

ow { owl   drown   howl
     bow   tower   flower

7. It has a stem and petals _____

8. A high building _____

9. To bend forward _____

10. The name of a bird _____

11. We may — in deep water _____

12. Dogs and wolves do this _____

4

On the farm

hen   cock   goat   dog

cat   barn   stack

tractor   pond   duck

1. _____
2. _____
3. _____
4. _____
5. _____

6. _____
7. _____
8. _____
9. _____
10. _____

Score

5

er

---

her   jerk   fern   term

---

1. Holidays come at the end
   of —   _____

2. A plant   _____

3. She ate — dinner   _____

4. Pull sharply   _____

or {
  horns   born   worn   corn
  storm   form   stork   port
}

5. A bird with long legs   _____

6. Rain and strong winds
   make a —   _____

7. It grows in the farmer's
   fields   _____

8. She was — in 1972   _____

9. A ship sails into this   _____

10. A bull has two of these   _____

11. Susan has — this dress for a
    long time   _____

12. Which — are you in at school?   _____

6

fir   bird   shirt
stir   girl   first

1. A sparrow is a —   _____

2. A tree with leaves like needles   _____

3. When we make gravy we — it   _____

4. The — wore a pretty dress   _____

5. —, second, third   _____

6. David put on a clean —   _____

ur { hurl   curls   curtain   turn   burnt   turkey

7. Elizabeth had — in her hair   _____

8. Move around   _____

9. If you play with fire you
may be —   _____

10. It hangs at the window   _____

11. At Christmas we often eat — _____

12. To throw   _____

sh

shell   shoes   ship
shop   shelf   sharp

1. We buy sweets from the —   _____
2. For putting things on   _____
3. Worn on the feet   _____
4. It sails across the sea   _____
5. A snail has one on its back   _____
6. A pin has a — point   _____

ch { chat   chop   chin   chips   chest   church

7. A part of the face   _____
8. A building   _____
9. A friendly talk   _____
10. A big box   _____
11. You — wood with an axe   _____
12. Often eaten with fish   _____

ee

bee   beech   deer
see   steel   peel

1. An animal with big horns   _____
2. A strong metal   _____
3. The name of a tree   _____
4. The skin of an orange or lemon   _____
5. It makes honey for us   _____
6. We — with our eyes   _____

oo { pools   wood   soot
     shoot   good   stoop }

7. Black and found in chimneys   _____
8. To bend forward   _____
9. Lots of trees   _____
10. To fire a gun   _____
11. Not bad   _____
12. The rain makes these   _____

9

Eaten

cheese	celery	bread	toast
butter	grapes	apples	
buns	cabbage	carrots	

1. _____   6. _____

2. _____   7. _____

3. _____   8. _____

4. _____   9. _____

5. _____   10. _____

Score

> tail   chain   wait
>
> rain   drain   pain

1. Water from the clouds   _____

2. Rings of metal joined together   _____

3. I will — for my Mum to come back   _____

4. A dog wags its —   _____

5. Water runs into a —   _____

6. We sometimes have a — when we are poorly   _____

ea   sea   team   easy

       tea   hear   tears

7. There are 11 footballers in a —   _____

8. We — with our ears   _____

9. We pour this from a pot   _____

10. These come when we cry   _____

11. Ships sail across the —   _____

12. Not hard   _____

oa

> boat soap road
> oats goals coat

1. Footballers try to score — _____
2. Motor-cars travel on the — _____
3. Something we wear _____
4. Used for washing our hands _____
5. A small ship _____
6. Horses like to eat — _____

oi { soil oil boil coins join point }

7. A kettle is used to — water _____
8. Money, but not banknotes _____
9. A needle has a sharp — _____
10. Fasten together _____
11. Put — on your bicycle to make it go better _____
12. Plants grow in the — _____

12

ou

out   round   shout
hour   found   clouds

1. Dark ones often bring rain   _____

2. To speak in a very loud voice   _____

3. David — a present near his bed   _____

4. Not in   _____

5. Sixty minutes are the same as one —   _____

6. The shape of a ring   _____

ay { days   pray   May

       lays   play   hay

7. A hen — eggs   _____

8. Horses eat —   _____

9. After lessons we go out to —   _____

10. To say prayers   _____

11. The fifth month of the year   _____

12. There are seven — in a week   _____

ack

back   Jack   sack   black

1. Father Christmas carries a — _____

2. You lean — in your seat _____

3. A boy's name _____

4. A colour _____

eck { deck   neck   pecks   speck

5. A bird does this _____

6. A part of the body _____

7. A sailor walks on the — _____

8. A tiny bit _____

ick { pick   lick   chick   sick

9. Poorly _____

10. A baby bird _____

11. Tom was told to — up the
    suitcase _____

12. On hot days it is fun to — an
    icecream _____

14

Worn

shoe   sock   jersey   glove
beret   sandal   jeans
scarf   blazer   dressing-gown

1. _____   6. _____

2. _____   7. _____

3. _____   8. _____

4. _____   9. _____

5. _____   10. _____

Score _____

ock

rock   lock   sock   cock

1. A key fits into this   _____

2. Worn on the foot   _____

3. A father bird   _____

4. A big stone   _____

uck ⎰ luck   suck
    ⎱ duck   stuck

5. The baby began to — his bottle   _____

6. I wish you good —   _____

7. The name of a bird   _____

8. John — the stamp on the
   letter   _____

ang ⎰ rang   gang
    ⎱ hang   sang

9. A group of people   _____

10. The blackbird — sweetly   _____

11. The bell — loudly   _____

12. Let's — the picture on this wall   _____

16

ing

ring   king   sting   wings

1. Wasps and bees can do this   _____

2. It is worn on a finger   _____

3. He wears a crown   _____

4. For flying   _____

ong { long   belong   songs   among

5. We sing these   _____

6. A rabbit has — ears   _____

7. She sat — the other girls   _____

8. Does this hat — to you?   _____

ung { sung   rung   hung   stung

9. Elizabeth was — by a wasp   _____

10. The bell was — at four o'clock   _____

11. The wet shirt — on the line   _____

12. Have they — their song?   _____

17

—e

cane   tape   sale
lane   gale   fade

1. A narrow road   _____

2. A strong wind   _____

3. The sun makes the colours in the curtains —   _____

4. Things are cheaper in a —   _____

5. A narrow strip of cloth   _____

6. A thin stick   _____

—e { dive   pile   side   wipe   ride   time }

7. To rub with a cloth   _____

8. To go headfirst into water   _____

9. What — will tea be ready, Mum?   _____

10. Jill can — a horse   _____

11. A heap   _____

12. Our garage stands at the — of the house   _____

18

> hole   robe   sole
>
> bone   pole   poke

1. The bottom of your shoe   _____

2. A long piece of wood   _____

3. A long dress   _____

4. A mouse lives in a —   _____

5. To push your finger into something   _____

6. A dog likes a —   _____

---e { tube   true   tune   blue   glue   flute

7. Used to stick things   _____

8. Jim hummed a little — to himself   _____

9. I like — stories best   _____

10. We squeeze toothpaste from a —   _____

11. The tune was played on a —   _____

12. A colour   _____

Help in the kitchen

table   mother   mixing bowl
rolling-pin   scales   apron
milk   kettle   kitten   cooker

1. _____   6. _____
2. _____   7. _____
3. _____   8. _____
4. _____   9. _____
5. _____   10. _____

Score

Months

May	March	November	October
June	July	September	January
April	August	December	February

1. What is the first month of the year? _____

2.   second _____

3.   third _____

4.   fourth _____

5.   fifth _____

6.   sixth _____

7.   seventh _____

8.   eighth _____

9.   ninth _____

10.   tenth _____

11.   eleventh _____

12.   twelfth _____

hitting	scatter	clatter
pretty	mutter	fatter	cotton

1. Used with a needle _____
2. The sound cups and saucers make _____
3. Nice to look at _____
4. Bigger and rounder _____
5. To throw all over the place _____
6. To speak in a low voice _____
7. Smacking _____

wa { was   wasp   war   water

wash   swan   watch   wants

8. Fighting between armies _____
9. To clean with water _____
10. A large graceful bird _____
11. Like a bee and it stings _____
12. I did not know I — late _____
13. Used for telling the time _____
14. Mary — a doll for Christmas _____
15. A drink _____

qu

| quick | quite | queer | quarter | quiet |

1. Strange   _____
2. ¼   _____
3. Fast   _____
4. Not noisy   _____
5. He told her that Christopher was — a clever boy   _____

ie | chief   field   piece   friend   shields

6. Knights carried them   _____
7. Another word for a part   _____
8. A word meaning the leader   _____
9. A farmer puts his animals into this   _____
10. A pal   _____

ui | suit   fruit   bruise   juice   biscuit

11. A dark patch on the skin   _____
12. The — from an orange is lovely to drink   _____
13. Apples, oranges and grapes are all different kinds of —   _____
14. Often eaten with a cup of tea   _____
15. The rain had spoilt a — of clothes   _____

23

Days

Tuesday Saturday Wednesday Thursday Monday

1. It comes after Wednesday   _____
2. The day after Friday   _____
3. On Pancake — we eat pancakes   _____
4. The day before Tuesday   _____
5. The day before Thursday   _____

oy { boy   annoy   enjoy   toys   oyster

6. Father Christmas seems to bring lots of these.   _____
7. To tease   _____
8. A shellfish   _____
9. Not a girl but a —   _____
10. To have a good time   _____

ept { wept   kept   swept   slept   crept

11. Went on sleeping   _____
12. Did not give away   _____
13. I — quietly upstairs to bed   _____
14 Cried   _____
15. Used a sweeping brush   _____

24

Fun on the beach

pier   lighthouse   seagull
boat   bucket   spade   sand-castle
towel   seaweed   swimsuit

1. _____	6. _____
2. _____	7. _____
3. _____	8. _____
4. _____	9. _____
5. _____	10. _____

Score

e
| bake | rake | wake |
| care | tame | share |
behave

1. A garden tool   _____

2. A tiger is wild, but a dog
   is —   _____

3. Always take — when crossing
   a road   _____

4. Cook   _____

5. Sh! Don't — the baby   _____

6. If you — yourself, you may
   stay up late   _____

7. A part of something   _____

¢ + ing
| baking | raking | caring | sharing |
| taming | waking | having | behaving |

8. Many children are good at
   — their sweets with others   _____

9. Taking care   _____

10. Opening your eyes after
    sleep   _____

11. Making a wild animal less
    wild   _____

12. Using a rake   _____

13. The class was — well   _____

14. Cooking   _____

15. Ian is — a birthday party   _____

26

e

ride	dine	hide	dive
ice	like	wipe	

1. To travel on a horse is
   to — it   _____

2. Frozen water   _____

3. To go down headfirst   _____

4. To eat your dinner   _____

5. Rub with a cloth   _____

6. To keep out of sight   _____

7. I — icecream   _____

¢ + ing {
| dining | riding | hiding | diving |
| icing | liking | wiping | giving |
}

8. Keeping out of sight   _____

9. Made of sugar   _____

10. Travelling on horseback   _____

11. Dinner was in the — room   _____

12. The teacher was — out books   _____

13. Rubbing with a cloth   _____

14. Going headfirst into water   _____

15. Enjoying   _____

e

> poke   doze   hope
>
> joke   store   love   come

1. I — it will stop raining   _____

2. Can you — out to play?   _____

3. A light sleep   _____

4. It hurts to — a finger in
   your eye   _____

5. A trick   _____

6. I would — to have a holiday   _____

7. Tins of food are often kept
   in a — cupboard   _____

¢ + ing {
poking   hoping   dozing   joking

storing   boring   loving   coming
}

8. My friend is — to tea   _____

9. Playing tricks   _____

10. Kate is — for snow tomorrow   _____

11. Dull and not interesting   _____

12. Kind   _____

13. Simon was — a stick into
    the hole   _____

14. Having a light sleep   _____

15. Putting things away until later   _____

e

| tune | tube | cure | prune | use |

1. Toothpaste is sold in a — _____
2. The doctor found a — for the disease _____
3. My Dad taught me to — a saw _____
4. It's a song with a merry — _____
5. A dried plum _____

¢ + ing { using   tubing   pruning   tuning   curing

6. Inside a tyre there is rubber — _____
7. Dr. Brown is — the lad of his spots _____
8. Mrs Jones is — her washing machine _____
9. Father was busy — the roses _____
10. An old man was — our piano _____

ff { toffee   coffee   stiff   staff   off

11. The light was switched — _____
12. The teachers at a school _____
13. A sticky sweet _____
14. A drink _____
15. Does not bend _____

Birthday party

cards   balloons   cake   candles
paper hat   presents   cracker
clock   sideboard   toffees

1. _____   6. _____

2. _____   7. _____

3. _____   8. _____

4. _____   9. _____

5. _____   10. _____

Score

Numbers

> two   four   seven   one
> six   five   three

1. $7 - 6$ _____
2. $8 \div 4$ _____
3. $9 \div 3$ _____
4. 2×2 _____
5. Half a dozen _____
6. $2 + 3$ _____
7. $4 + 3$ _____

aw { paw   saw   draw   law   jaw   raw   hawk   straw }

8. To make a picture with a pencil _____
9. A part of the face _____
10. A dog's foot _____
11. Not cooked _____
12. A tool used for cutting wood _____
13. Animals sleep on it _____
14. A bird _____
15. Parking on a zebra crossing is against the — _____

mm

summer	mummy	dummy
slammed	drummer	hammer	tummy

1. We like to fill this with food   _____
2. Only a baby would suck this   _____
3. Mother   _____
4. After the spring comes the —   _____
5. A tool for hitting nails   _____
6. He plays the drums   _____
7. Shut with a bang   _____

nn { pinned   grinned   running   cunning

winner   winning   dinner   thinner }

8. If Arthur came first he was the —   _____
9. If you don't eat you will grow —   _____
10. The main meal of the day   _____
11. Fastened with a pin   _____
12. Faster than walking   _____
13. Sly   _____
14. For — the race his aunt gave him a present   _____
15. Tom — all over his face   _____

y

fairy	many	daisy	
baby	diary	berry	lady

1. A flower   _____
2. A fruit   _____
3. A tiny child   _____
4. A book you write in   _____
5. A woman   _____
6. Often at the top of a
   Christmas tree   _____
7. A lot   _____

kn { knot   knew   knits   knee

     knock   knight   knife   kneel

8. A sharp tool   _____
9. He rode on horseback   _____
10. Hit   _____
11. You tie this   _____
12. Mary — all her tables   _____
13. To go down on your knees   _____
14. A part of the leg   _____
15. Mother does it with two
    needles   _____

ies

> fairies　　lollies　　daisies
>
> babies　　diaries　　ladies　　berries

1. Sweets _____

2. Tiny children _____

3. Fruits _____

4. Flowers _____

5. These are supposed to live in 'Fairyland' _____

6. Women _____

7. Books in which we write what happens _____

all { tall　stall　ball　all　wall　hall　call　fall

8. Everyone _____

9. Tumble _____

10. The — was packed for the meeting _____

11. Built of bricks and cement _____

12. Shout _____

13. A kind of shop in a market _____

14. It is round and used in games _____

15. High _____

Spring-cleaning

saddle   handlebars   spokes
tyre   mudguard   handpump
oilcan   spanner   chain   pedal

1. _____
2. _____
3. _____
4. _____
5. _____

6. _____
7. _____
8. _____
9. _____
10. _____

Score

six	axe	boxes
wax	sixty	foxes	sixteen

1. A candle is made of this   _____
2. 6   _____
3. 16   _____
4. 60   _____
5. For putting things in   _____
6. Animals with bushy tails   _____
7. Used for chopping down trees   _____

ea {
head   bread   dead   meadow

breath   lead   read   weather
}

8. Not alive   _____
9. The air we breathe out is our —   _____
10. At six we heard the — forecast   _____
11. A food made from flour   _____
12. John put his cap on his —   _____
13. The teacher — us a story   _____
14. A field of grass   _____
15. A very heavy metal   _____

ied

tried   fried   cried   lied   died

1. Shed tears   _____

2. Cooked in a frying pan   _____

3. Worked very hard   _____

4. Did not live   _____

5. Did not tell the truth   _____

le { thistle   freckle   little   handle   prickle

      candle   bottle   rifle   trifle   rattle

6. Milk comes in this   _____

7. Small   _____

8. A baby's plaything   _____

9. A prickly weed   _____

10. A gooseberry bush has many
    a sharp one   _____

11. Open the door with this   _____

12. A brown mark on the face   _____

13. Often eaten at a party   _____

14. It gives us light   _____

15. A gun carried by soldiers   _____

37

ace

face	ace	trace
lace	race	place	pace

1. Used to tie your shoe   _____
2. To go fast   _____
3. A step or stride   _____
4. To go over the lines with a pencil   _____
5. Show me the — where it hurts   _____
6. The front part of the head   _____
7. The 'one' in a pack of cards   _____

bb { rubber   cobbler   rubbing   bubbles

robber   pebble   wobble }

8. A boy's name   _____
9. If you — on a bicycle you may fall off   _____
10. Small children blow these   _____
11. A small stone   _____
12. He mends shoes   _____
13. A thief   _____
14. It takes out pencil marks   _____
15. Polishing   _____

38

ight

fight	light	night
sight	might	right	tight

1. Turn left not — _____

2. The dark hours _____

3. A battle _____

4. His shoes hurt because they were too — _____

5. The trees and lakes were a lovely — _____

6. At night we switch on the — _____

7. 'It — snow tomorrow,' said Jane _____

Pets { rabbit   kitten   canary   goldfish
       parrot   mouse   horse   budgerigar

8. A yellow singing bird _____

9. A fish _____

10. A young cat _____

11. A big bird which often talks _____

12. This lives in a hutch _____

13. His short name is 'budgie' _____

14. The biggest of them all _____

15. A small animal with a long tail _____

39

Trouble at the supermarket

toddler   cereal packet   old gentleman
walking stick   assistant   tinned fruit
basket   handbag   loaf   coffee

1. _____   6. _____
2. _____   7. _____
3. _____   8. _____
4. _____   9. _____
5. _____   10. _____

Score

wh

whip   which   whisper
wheel   whale   white   wheat

1. A huge sea-creature   _____
2. The colour of snow   _____
3. A lion-trainer may use one   _____
4. To talk very softly   _____
5. A car carries a spare one   _____
6. Flour is made from this   _____
7. A word often used when asking questions   _____

Buildings { office   house   hotel   station
school   garage   church   hospital }

8. A building for a car   _____
9. Papers and typewriters are found here   _____
10. A place to stay on our holidays perhaps   _____
11. God's house   _____
12. We learn our lessons here   _____
13. Ill people often go here   _____
14. The building we live in   _____
15. Trains stop at this   _____

The Body

eyes	knee	throat	mouth	knuckle
ears	wrist	ankle	fingers	shoulder
hair	head	thumb	elbow	eyebrows

1. We have eight of these and two thumbs   _____

2. A joint in the arm   _____

3. A joint halfway down the leg   _____

4. Where the brain is   _____

5. A part of the finger   _____

6. Hairs just above the eyes   _____

7. Used for listening   _____

8. Used for seeing   _____

9. This grows on the head   _____

10. The tongue and the teeth are in this   _____

11. Used for swallowing   _____

12. This joins the hand and the arm   _____

13. Where the arm joins the body   _____

14. We have one on each hand   _____

15. This joint helps us to move our foot   _____

al

canal	final	metal	animal
petal	signal	sandal	hospital

1. Engine drivers look out for this _____

2. A kind of shoe _____

3. A building for people who are ill _____

4. A four-legged creature _____

5. A waterway _____

6. A word meaning last _____

7. Made of iron and steel _____

8. Part of a flower _____

Numbers { eight   eleven   twelve   nineteen   twenty   fifteen   thirteen }

9. 11 _____

10. A dozen _____

11. 4 × 2 _____

12. A score _____

13. 5 × 3 _____

14. 19 _____

15. 13 _____

43

> models   kennel   chapel   quarrel
>
> travel   parcel   shovel   angel   tunnel

1. A church   _____

2. A tool   _____

3. Package brought by the postman   _____

4. Children make these from wood and cardboard   _____

5. A home for a dog   _____

6. An underground passage   _____

7. To argue angrily   _____

8. Move from one place to another   _____

9. A messenger from God   _____

str { straw   street   strict   stream   straight   stranger

10. A person not known to you   _____

11. A road in a town   _____

12. Stalks from corn   _____

13. A small river   _____

14. Stern   _____

15. Not crooked   _____

The quarrel

poodle   fox terrier   lead
collar   pavement   kerb   manhole cover
pillar-box   trilby hat   policeman

1. _____   6. _____
2. _____   7. _____
3. _____   8. _____
4. _____   9. _____
5. _____   10. _____

Score _____

gu

> guitar   guide   guest   guard   guilty

1. A visitor to your home   _____
2. Protect   _____
3. Having done something wrong   _____
4. A musical instrument   _____
5. One who shows the way   _____

ough | cough   enough   rough   tough

6. Strong   _____
7. Plenty   _____
8. Not smooth   _____
9. Often follows a cold   _____

air | pair   aircraft   upstairs
dairy   fairies   repair

10. Aeroplanes   _____
11. Plural of 'fairy'   _____
12. A shop which sells milk   _____
13. Two of the same kind   _____
14. Peter went — in his dressing gown   _____
15. A word meaning mend   _____

46

ur

> further   purple   curved   burn   Saturday
> return   surprise   burglar   turnip   Thursday

---

1. Go back _____

2. He robs houses and shops _____

3. A vegetable _____

4. If today is Tuesday the day
   after tomorrow will be — _____

5. Put in the fire _____

6. A colour _____

7. A word meaning farther _____

8. Bent _____

9. An unexpected happening _____

10. The last day of the week _____

ying { dying   drying   flying   frying   trying

11. Cooking _____

12. Moving through the air _____

13. Working hard _____

14. Losing life _____

15. Getting rid of the water _____

47

ves

| halves | wives | leaves | thieves | wolves |
| calves | loaves | knives | shelves | themselves |

1. Married women _____
2. Used for putting things on _____
3. For cutting _____
4. The teacher told them to behave — _____
5. Farm animals _____
6. Wild animals _____
7. People who steal _____
8. In the autumn they are swept up _____
9. Cakes of bread _____
10. Two — make a whole one _____

ion { nation relation portion direction mention

11. The horse galloped in that — _____
12. A people _____
13. A member of your family _____
14. A part _____
15. To speak about _____

48

tch

watch	ditch	pitch	matches	scratches
fetch	itches	stretch	kitchen	stitches
hutch	switch	witch	butcher	patch

1. We buy our meat from him _____

2. Martin needed three — in his leg _____

3. A piece of cloth to cover a hole _____

4. A cat's claws will leave these on your skin _____

5. When struck they burn _____

6. A room for cooking and washing up the pots _____

7. To bring _____

8. To pull out and make longer _____

9. A trench for water _____

10. She is said to ride on a broomstick _____

11. A house for a rabbit _____

12. Tickles _____

13. The team rolled the cricket — _____

14. It puts on the light _____

15. It gives us the time _____

Help in the garden

greenhouse   fence   wheelbarrow
leaves   rake   sundial   bonfire
trowel   sunflowers   rockery

1. _____   6. _____
2. _____   7. _____
3. _____   8. _____
4. _____   9. _____
5. _____   10. _____

Score

50

purrs	narrow	worried	carriage	marriage
arrow	hurries	arrange	porridge	tomorrow
error	mirror	arrested	arrived	strawberries

1. Shot from a bow   _____

2. A wedding   _____

3. For carrying people   _____

4. A breakfast food made from oats   _____

5. To put things in order   _____

6. The day which comes after today   _____

7. The gate was too — for the tractor   _____

8. If a cat —, it is happy   _____

9. Troubled about something   _____

10. Goes quickly   _____

11. Fruit   _____

12. A looking-glass   _____

13. Caught by the police   _____

14. The Scouts — home wet through   _____

15. A mistake   _____

cork   pork   forty
worm   forgets   snore   fortnight

1. It makes holes in the soil _____

2. Do you — when you are
   asleep? _____

3. Fits into a bottle _____

4. 20 × 2 _____

5. Meat from a pig _____

6. Does not remember _____

7. Fourteen days _____

or { motor   sailor   doctor   corridor

actor   junior   tractor   emperor }

8. A passage _____

9. A person who acts _____

10. A child under about 11 years
    of age _____

11. Farmers use it when ploughing
    the fields _____

12. An engine _____

13. We go to him when we are ill _____

14. A seaman _____

15. A king who roles over an
    empire _____

wr

> wrist   wrong   wrapped
>
> wreck   wriggle   wrinkles   writing

1. It joins the arm to the hand   _____
2. His mother was — a letter   _____
3. To twist and turn   _____
4. A ship broken up by the sea   _____
5. Covered in paper   _____
6. Small lines on the face   _____
7. Not right   _____

ey
{
money   honey   chimney
monkey   donkey
}

8. An animal rather like a man   _____
9. For the smoke to go up   _____
10. Coins   _____
11. A sweet food   _____
12. Like a horse, but has long ears   _____

eight
{
weight   height
eight
}

13. How high a thing is   _____
14. 8   _____
15. How heavy a thing is   _____

ce

twice	palace	saucer	piece	policeman
iceberg	grocer	notice	peace	lettuce

1. A house for a king _____
2. A large floating lump of ice _____
3. A teacup stands on this _____
4. A part of something _____
5. He keeps order _____
6. Two times _____
7. A shopkeeper _____
8. Often pinned up on a board to be read _____
9. Quietness _____
10. Vegetable used in salads _____

nch { lunch finch branch ranch pinch

11. The arm of a tree _____
12. A bird _____
13. To nip _____
14. A meal _____
15. Cowboys are found on this _____

54

At the circus

whip   ringmaster   bareback rider
clown   bucket   umbrella   acrobat
trapeze   tightrope walker   juggler

1. _____   6. _____
2. _____   7. _____
3. _____   8. _____
4. _____   9. _____
5. _____   10. _____

Score

roller	called	collar	yellow	swallow
silly	really	willow	tallest	woollen
till	ballet	follow	village	William

1. A boy's name   _____

2. Foolish   _____

3. A tree   _____

4. Shops keep their money in this   _____

5. A colour   _____

6. A dog wears one round the neck   _____

7. A boy — Jonathan scored two goals   _____

8. Truly   _____

9. To come after   _____

10. A bird   _____

11. A place not big enough to be a town   _____

12. Made of wool   _____

13. A word meaning the highest   _____

14. Dancing to music on a stage   _____

15. A garden tool   _____

ck

struck	wicked	kicked	stockings
pockets	jacket	rockets	blackboard
cricket	pickle	chicken	mackintosh

1. They fire these into the air   _____

2. A summer game   _____

3. A farm bird   _____

4. Evil   _____

5. A raincoat   _____

6. It adds a tang to food   _____

7. A word meaning hit   _____

8. A short coat   _____

9. Hit with the foot   _____

10. Chalk is used to write on this   _____

11. Worn on the legs   _____

12. In coats and trousers for carrying things in   _____

tele { telephone   telescope   television

13. The short name is TV   _____

14. Used for studying the stars   _____

15. Used for speaking to people   _____

ly

tidily	loudly	safely	happily	suddenly
slowly	bravely	easily	kindly	honestly
quietly	sadly	gently	poorly	lovely

1. All at once _____
2. Beautiful _____
3. Full of happiness _____
4. Taking a long time _____
5. Neatly _____
6. In a loud way _____
7. Without difficulty _____
8. In a kind way _____
9. Without much sound _____
10. In a safe way _____
11. Truthfully _____
12. In a gentle manner _____
13. In bad health _____
14. In a sad way _____
15. With courage _____

dresses	princess	assist	useless	address
pressed	illness	glasses	passage	messenger

1. We drink out of these _____
2. Worn by girls _____
3. Daughter of a king or queen _____
4. A corridor _____
5. Help _____
6. It is written on an envelope _____
7. Of no use _____
8. Pushed hard _____
9. Sickness _____
10. One who takes a message _____

mb { bomber   plumber   climb   dumb   limbs }

11. Arms and legs _____
12. To go upwards _____
13. A war plane _____
14. Unable to speak _____
15. He repairs pipes and windows _____

Holiday ahead

caravan   roof-rack   rubber dinghy   corgi
sleeping-bag   suitcase   vacuum flask
beach ball   cricket bat   wellington boots

1. _____   6. _____
2. _____   7. _____
3. _____   8. _____
4. _____   9. _____
5. _____   10. _____

Score

ed

called	sharpened	roared	travelled	listened
entered	fastened	prayed	talked	frightened

1. Fixed _____
2. Talked to God _____
3. Used his ears _____
4. Made a noise like a lion _____
5. Named _____
6. Dad — the carving knife _____
7. Afraid _____
8. Came in _____
9. Spoke _____
10. Moved from one place to another _____

ful { awful beautiful useful handful careful

11. Lovely to look at _____
12. As much as can be held in one hand _____
13. Not careless _____
14. Helpful _____
15. The burning ship was an — sight _____

pp

supper	clapping	disappear	
hopping	pepper	stopped	disappointed

1. Not moving   _____
2. Going on one foot in jumps   _____
3. A meal   _____
4. Sad   _____
5. To go out of sight   _____
6. It can make you sneeze   _____
7. Striking the hands together   _____

ought | fought   ought   brought
         thoughts   bought

8. Tom — a lollipop from the shop   _____
9. Ideas   _____
10. We — to visit the dentist twice a year   _____
11. Struggled   _____
12. Fetched   _____

aught | taught   daughter
       caught

13. Captured   _____
14. A girl   _____
15. His fall — him to be careful   _____

Tricky Ones

safety   bicycle   queue   hymns   cupboard
choir   library   yacht   colours   leopard
tongue   theatre   suite   Elizabeth   orchestra

1. Sung in church   _____
2. Place for storing things   _____
3. A girl's name   _____
4. A line of waiting people   _____
5. A set of furniture   _____
6. Plays are acted here   _____
7. A band in a theatre   _____
8. For tasting and talking   _____
9. Cycle with two wheels   _____
10. For sailing   _____
11. A group of singers   _____
12. We borrow books from here   _____
13. His costume was fastened with a — pin   _____
14. Fierce animal in cat family   _____
15. Blue, red, yellow and green   _____

	(1)		(2)		(3)
1.	rat	1.	lip	1.	mug
2.	bat	2.	pin	2.	hug
3.	gas	3.	tin	3.	nut
4.	lad	4.	sit	4.	bull
5.	hat	5.	bit	5.	rub
6.	bag	6.	hit	6.	cub
7.	hen	7.	cot	7.	fun
8.	bed	8.	dog	8.	dry
9.	ten	9.	fog	9.	why
10.	peg	10.	hop	10.	try
11.	pen	11.	log	11.	fry
12.	leg	12.	top	12.	cry

	(4)		(5)		(6)
1.	jar	1.	stack	1.	term
2.	far	2.	barn	2.	fern
3.	star	3.	duck	3.	her
4.	car	4.	pond	4.	jerk
5.	tar	5.	tractor	5.	stork
6.	bar	6.	cat	6.	storm
7.	flower	7.	cock	7.	corn
8.	tower	8.	hen	8.	born
9.	bow	9.	goat	9.	port
10.	owl	10.	dog	10.	horns
11.	drown			11.	worn
12.	howl			12.	form

(7)	(8)	(9)
1. bird	1. shop	1. deer
2. fir	2. shelf	2. steel
3. stir	3. shoes	3. beech
4. girl	4. ship	4. peel
5. first	5. shell	5. bee
6. shirt	6. sharp	6. see
7. curls	7. chin	7. soot
8. turn	8. church	8. stoop
9. burnt	9. chat	9. wood
10. curtain	10. chest	10. shoot
11. turkey	11. chop	11. good
12. hurl	12. chips	12. pools

(10)	(11)	(12)
1. bread	1. rain	1. goals
2. toast	2. chain	2. road
3. celery	3. wait	3. coat
4. apples	4. tail	4. soap
5. cheese	5. drain	5. boat
6. grapes	6. pain	6. oats
7. cabbage	7. team	7. boil
8. buns	8. hear	8. coins
9. butter	9. tea	9. point
10. carrots	10. tears	10. join
	11. sea	11. oil
	12. easy	12. soil

(13)
1. clouds
2. shout
3. found
4. out
5. hour
6. round
7. lays
8. hay
9. play
10. pray
11. May
12. days

(14)
1. sack
2. back
3. Jack
4. black
5. pecks
6. neck
7. deck
8. speck
9. sick
10. chick
11. pick
12. lick

(15)
1. jersey
2. dressing-gown
3. jeans
4. blazer
5. sandal
6. scarf
7. beret
8. shoe
9. glove
10. sock

(16)
1. lock
2. sock
3. cock
4. rock
5. suck
6. luck
7. duck
8. stuck
9. gang
10. sang
11. rang
12. hang

(17)
1. sting
2. ring
3. king
4. wings
5. songs
6. long
7. among
8. belong
9. stung
10. rung
11. hung
12. sung

(18)
1. lane
2. gale
3. fade
4. sale
5. tape
6. cane
7. wipe
8. dive
9. time
10. ride
11. pile
12. side

(19)
1. sole
2. pole
3. robe
4. hole
5. poke
6. bone
7. glue
8. tune
9. true
10. tube
11. flute
12. blue

(20)
1. kettle
2. cooker
3. mother
4. mixing bowl
5. scales
6. rolling-pin
7. milk
8. table
9. kitten
10. apron

(21)
1. January
2. February
3. March
4. April
5. May
6. June
7. July
8. August
9. September
10. October
11. November
12. December

(22)
1. cotton
2. clatter
3. pretty
4. fatter
5. scatter
6. mutter
7. hitting
8. war
9. wash
10. swan
11. wasp
12. was
13. watch
14. wants
15. water

(23)
1. queer
2. quarter
3. quick
4. quiet
5. quite
6. shields
7. piece
8. chief
9. field
10. friend
11. bruise
12. juice
13. fruit
14. biscuit
15. suit

(24)
1. Thursday
2. Saturday
3. Tuesday
4. Monday
5. Wednesday
6. toys
7. annoy
8. oyster
9. boy
10. enjoy
11. slept
12. kept
13. crept
14. wept
15. swept

(25)
1. lighthouse
2. seagull
3. pier
4. boat
5. towel
6. seaweed
7. sand-castle
8. bucket
9. swimsuit
10. spade

(26)
1. rake
2. tame
3. care
4. bake
5. wake
6. behave
7. share
8. sharing
9. caring
10. waking
11. taming
12. raking
13. behaving
14. baking
15. having

(27)
1. ride
2. ice
3. dive
4. dine
5. wipe
6. hide
7. like
8. hiding
9. icing
10. riding
11. dining
12. giving
13. wiping
14. diving
15. liking

(28)
1. hope
2. come
3. doze
4. poke
5. joke
6. love
7. store
8. coming
9. joking
10. hoping
11. boring
12. loving
13. poking
14. dozing
15. storing

(29)
1. tube
2. cure
3. use
4. tune
5. prune
6. tubing
7. curing
8. using
9. pruning
10. tuning
11. off
12. staff
13. toffee
14. coffee
15. stiff

(30)
1. balloons
2. cards
3. clock
4. paper hat
5. sideboard
6. candles
7. cake
8. toffees
9. cracker
10. presents

(31)
1. one
2. two
3. three
4. four
5. six
6. five
7. seven
8. draw
9. jaw
10. paw
11. raw
12. saw
13. straw
14. hawk
15. law

(32)
1. tummy
2. dummy
3. mummy
4. summer
5. hammer
6. drummer
7. slammed
8. winner
9. thinner
10. dinner
11. pinned
12. running
13. cunning
14. winning
15. grinned

(33)
1. daisy
2. berry
3. baby
4. diary
5. lady
6. fairy
7. many
8. knife
9. knight
10. knock
11. knot
12. knew
13. kneel
14. knee
15. knits

(34)
1. lollies
2. babies
3. berries
4. daisies
5. fairies
6. ladies
7. diaries
8. all
9. fall
10. hall
11. wall
12. call
13. stall
14. ball
15. tall

(35)
1. saddle
2. handlebars
3. spokes
4. chain
5. pedal
6. tyre
7. spanner
8. mudguard
9. oilcan
10. handpump

(36)
1. wax
2. six
3. sixteen
4. sixty
5. boxes
6. foxes
7. axe
8. dead
9. breath
10. weather
11. bread
12. head
13. read
14. meadow
15. lead

(37)

1. cried
2. fried
3. tried
4. died
5. lied
6. bottle
7. little
8. rattle
9. thistle
10. prickle
11. handle
12. freckle
13. trifle
14. candle
15. rifle

(38)

1. lace
2. race
3. pace
4. trace
5. place
6. face
7. ace
8. Bobby
9. wobble
10. bubbles
11. pebble
12. cobbler
13. robber
14. rubber
15. rubbing

(39)

1. right
2. night
3. fight
4. tight
5. sight
6. light
7. might
8. canary
9. goldfish
10. kitten
11. parrot
12. rabbit
13. budgerigar
14. horse
15. mouse

(40)

1. tinned fruit
2. assistant
3. old gentleman
4. walking stick
5. toddler
6. cereal packet
7. handbag
8. coffee
9. basket
10. loaf

(41)

1. whale
2. white
3. whip
4. whisper
5. wheel
6. wheat
7. which
8. garage
9. office
10. hotel
11. church
12. school
13. hospital
14. house
15. station

(42)

1. fingers
2. elbow
3. knee
4. head
5. knuckle
6. eyebrows
7. ears
8. eyes
9. hair
10. mouth
11. throat
12. wrist
13. shoulder
14. thumb
15. ankle

(43)

1. signal
2. sandal
3. hospital
4. animal
5. canal
6. final
7. metal
8. petal
9. eleven
10. twelve
11. eight
12. twenty
13. fifteen
14. nineteen
15. thirteen

(44)

1. chapel
2. shovel
3. parcel
4. models
5. kennel
6. tunnel
7. quarrel
8. travel
9. angel
10. stranger
11. street
12. straw
13. stream
14. strict
15. straight

(45)

1. trilby hat
2. policeman
3. pillar-box
4. manhole cover
5. lead
6. collar
7. pavement
8. fox terrier
9. kerb
10. poodle

(46)

1. guest
2. guard
3. guilty
4. guitar
5. guide
6. tough
7. enough
8. rough
9. cough
10. aircraft
11. fairies
12. dairy
13. pair
14. upstairs
15. repair

(47)

1. return
2. burglar
3. turnip
4. Thursday
5. burn
6. purple
7. further
8. curved
9. surprise
10. Saturday
11. frying
12. flying
13. trying
14. dying
15. drying

(48)

1. wives
2. shelves
3. knives
4. themselves
5. calves
6. wolves
7. thieves
8. leaves
9. loaves
10. halves
11. direction
12. nation
13. relation
14. portion
15. mention

(49)

1. butcher
2. stitches
3. patch
4. scratches
5. matches
6. kitchen
7. fetch
8. stretch
9. ditch
10. witch
11. hutch
12. itches
13. pitch
14. switch
15. watch

(50)

1. greenhouse
2. sunflowers
3. fence
4. rake
5. bonfire
6. wheelbarrow
7. leaves
8. rockery
9. sundial
10. trowel

(51)

1. arrow
2. marriage
3. carriage
4. porridge
5. arrange
6. tomorrow
7. narrow
8. purrs
9. worried
10. hurries
11. strawberries
12. mirror
13. arrested
14. arrived
15. error

(52)

1. worm
2. snore
3. cork
4. forty
5. pork
6. forgets
7. fortnight
8. corridor
9. actor
10. junior
11. tractor
12. motor
13. doctor
14. sailor
15. emperor

(53)

1. wrist
2. writing
3. wriggle
4. wreck
5. wrapped
6. wrinkles
7. wrong
8. monkey
9. chimney
10. money
11. honey
12. donkey
13. height
14. eight
15. weight

(54)

1. palace
2. iceberg
3. saucer
4. piece
5. policeman
6. twice
7. grocer
8. notice
9. peace
10. lettuce
11. branch
12. finch
13. pinch
14. lunch
15. ranch

(55)
1. trapeze
2. umbrella
3. bareback rider
4. tightrope walker
5. acrobat
6. juggler
7. clown
8. bucket
9. whip
10. ringmaster

(56)
1. William
2. silly
3. willow
4. till
5. yellow
6. collar
7. called
8. really
9. follow
10. swallow
11. village
12. woollen
13. tallest
14. ballet
15. roller

(57)
1. rockets
2. cricket
3. chicken
4. wicked
5. mackintosh
6. pickle
7. struck
8. jacket
9. kicked
10. blackboard
11. stockings
12. pockets
13. television
14. telescope
15. telephone

(58)
1. suddenly
2. lovely
3. happily
4. slowly
5. tidily
6. loudly
7. easily
8. kindly
9. quietly
10. safely
11. honestly
12. gently
13. poorly
14. sadly
15. bravely

(59)
1. glasses
2. dresses
3. princess
4. passage
5. assist
6. address
7. useless
8. pressed
9. illness
10. messenger
11. limbs
12. climb
13. bomber
14. dumb
15. plumber

(60)
1. roof-rack
2. caravan
3. vacuum flask
4. sleeping-bag
5. rubber dinghy
6. suitcase
7. beach ball
8. cricket bat
9. wellington boots
10. corgi

(61)	(62)	(63)
1. fastened	1. stopped	1. hymns
2. prayed	2. hopping	2. cupboard
3. listened	3. supper	3. Elizabeth
4. roared	4. disappointed	4. queue
5. called	5. disappear	5. suite
6. sharpened	6. pepper	6. theatre
7. frightened	7. clapping	7. orchestra
8. entered	8. bought	8. tongue
9. talked	9. thoughts	9. bicycle
10. travelled	10. ought	10. yacht
11. beautiful	11. fought	11. choir
12. handful	12. brought	12. library
13. careful	13. caught	13. safety
14. useful	14. daughter	14. leopard
15. awful	15. taught	15. colours

Spelling
Quiz Book 2

CONTENTS

ie

piece	yield	priest	grieve	believe
chief	thief	pierce	shield	mischief
siege	niece	field	fierce	handkerchief

1. A part   _____

2. To feel sorrow   _____

3. To think of as true   _____

4. Your brother's or sister's daughter   _____

5. Carried for protection   _____

6. The head person   _____

7. To give in   _____

8. Animals graze in it   _____

9. To make a hole   _____

10. Savage   _____

11. One who steals   _____

12. A clergyman   _____

13. Naughtiness   _____

14. For wiping the nose   _____

15. The surrounding of a city by an army   _____

1

wr

wrath wrestling writhe wrapper wreckage
wren wretched wrong wreath wrist-watch

1. Paper around a sweet   _____

2. The broken pieces   _____

3. To twist about in pain   _____

4. Not right   _____

5. A word meaning anger   _____

6. Miserable   _____

7. A sport   _____

8. A small brown bird   _____

9. Jane's new — kept good time   _____

10. A ring or cross of flowers often sent to a funeral   _____

dge { hedge   fudge   hedgehog   sledge   bridge

11. A soft sweet   _____

12. Small animal covered with spines   _____

13. A fence of plants   _____

14. A way over a river or railway   _____

15. Is pulled across the snow   _____

2

camel   funnel   barrel   jewel   shovel

flannel   tunnel   panel   gospel   quarrel

1. A precious stone   _____

2. Round wooden container   _____

3. A kind of spade   _____

4. Animal with one or two humps on its back   _____

5. A tool used for pouring   _____

6. Underground passage   _____

7. A flat piece of wood, often in a door or wall   _____

8. The teaching of Christ   _____

9. Cloth   _____

10. To disagree   _____

ar {   sugar   beggar   mortar   collar   cellar

11. It is put between bricks   _____

12. A part of one's dress   _____

13. Used for sweetening   _____

14. A person who begs   _____

15. A room under a house   _____

3

ei

> eight   neigh   reign   height   weird
> weight   seize   heifer   neither   neighbour
> weigh   rein   their   foreign   neighbourhood

1. To find out how heavy a thing is _____

2. To rule _____

3. Belonging to another country _____

4. 2 × 4 _____

5. To grasp suddenly _____

6. Piece of metal used for weighing _____

7. Belonging to them _____

8. A person who lives near _____

9. Strap for guiding a horse _____

10. Strange _____

11. Not this one nor that _____

12. Sound made by a horse _____

13. A district _____

14. A young cow _____

15. How high a thing is _____

At the baths

swimming instructor   towel   swimsuit
spring-board   handrail   goggles
whistle   spectators   balcony   flippers

1. _____   6. _____
2. _____   7. _____
3. _____   8. _____
4. _____   9. _____
5. _____   10. _____

Score

haul	gaudy	saunter	autumn	sausages
sauce	August	author	laundry	autograph
vault	mauve	draught	saucer	saucepan

1. A season _____
2. Word meaning a writer _____
3. Showy _____
4. To stroll _____
5. Clothes are washed here _____
6. Added to food to make it tasty _____
7. It is put under a teacup _____
8. An underground room with an arched roof _____
9. To drag _____
10. A kitchen pan _____
11. Minced meat put into skins _____
12. A wind through a building _____
13. One's own signature _____
14. The eighth month _____
15. Light purple colour _____

tt

cottage   button   gutter   bottom   butterfly

1. A small house   _____
2. A winged insect   _____
3. Opposite of top   _____
4. Drain   _____
5. Used to fasten clothing   _____

ey {

valley   jersey   obeyed   spinney   Geoffrey

barley   turkey   parsley   journey   disobeyed

6. A pullover   _____
7. Low ground between hills   _____
8. A small bushy area   _____
9. Green and often decorates fish   _____
10. Wheat, oats and — are cereals   _____
11. To travel   _____
12. A boy's name   _____
13. A bird eaten at Christmas   _____
14. Did as he was told   _____
15. Did not do as he was told   _____

| lying | typist | hyphen | magnifying |
| dying | dyeing | rhyme | terrifying |

1. Frightening _____
2. Small line joining two words _____
3. Habit of telling untruths _____
4. We were able to read it with his — glass _____
5. Words in poems often — _____
6. One who uses a typewriter _____
7. Losing life _____
8. Putting colour into cloth _____

y { enemy   syrup   berry   poetry   rhythm   bury   symphony }

9. Regular beats _____
10. Poems _____
11. To cover in soil _____
12. A fruit _____
13. A sweet liquid _____
14. A foe _____
15. A piece of music _____

8

> rejoice joint oilfield ointment
> boiling coiled poisons voice loiter

1. If swallowed these are dangerous _____

2. The snake was — around a tree _____

3. Where oil is found _____

4. Be happy _____

5. Tea is made with — water _____

6. The butcher wrapped the — of meat _____

7. To linger _____

8. The sound from your throat _____

9. Heals sores _____

> calm psalms palm
> yolk folk chalk

10. Sacred songs in the Bible _____

11. A tree and also a part of the hand _____

12. The yellow part of an egg _____

13. We write on the blackboard with — _____

14. Peaceful _____

15. Another word for people _____

9

Slow movers

snail parachutist hedgehog invalid
cattle gypsy caravan tortoise
worm donkey plough

1. _____ 6. _____
2. _____ 7. _____
3. _____ 8. _____
4. _____ 9. _____
5. _____ 10. _____

Score

address	wedding	ladder	middle	suddenly
hidden	pudding	nodding	midday	saddle

1. A marriage   _____
2. The centre-point   _____
3. Eaten at dinner   _____
4. Written on an envelope _____
5. A seat on a horse   _____
6. Put out of sight   _____
7. Quickly   _____
8. Moving the head up and down _____
9. Noon   _____
10. You climb this   _____

bb { grabbed   cabbage   rubbish   scribble   ribbon }

11. A narrow strip of cloth _____
12. John was — from behind _____
13. A green vegetable   _____
14. The contents of a dustbin _____
15. To write carelessly   _____

tion

> station ration correction dictionary election
> position motion protection decoration
> invention

1. Place _____

2. The choosing of rulers by voting _____

3. A book of word meanings _____

4. Movement _____

5. It adds beauty _____

6. You board a train here _____

7. Something new, the first of its kind _____

8. The putting right of a sum, spelling or anything else _____

9. Your share of something which is scarce _____

10. A shield or defence _____

ous { famous   nervous   enormous   poisonous   jealous

11. Wanting what belongs to another _____

12. Easily scared or upset _____

13. Very well known _____

14. Huge _____

15. Harmful _____

Swiss	pressure	passengers	assembly	assistant
possess	business	passport	message	necessary

1. One who helps _____

2. A word meaning buying and selling _____

3. A gathering of people _____

4. Force _____

5. Booklet needed when travelling abroad _____

6. To have _____

7. The people of Switzerland _____

8. Information sent to a person _____

9. Our bus carries 32 — _____

10. A word meaning needed _____

ph { triumph pheasant orphan photograph phantom

11. A bird with a long tail _____

12. A child who has lost its parents _____

13. A ghost _____

14. Victory _____

15. A picture made with a camera _____

figure	murder	murmur	furniture
turban	pursue	purpose	turquoise

1. To kill   _____
2. A head-dress   _____
3. To mutter   _____
4. Greenish-blue   _____
5. To chase   _____
6. A shape or number   _____
7. He didn't do it on —   _____
8. Tables, chairs, etc.   _____

qu { conquer   queue   quoit   conqueror
     quantity   query   quill

9. To defeat   _____
10. One who defeats another   _____
11. What — of these would you like?   _____
12. A feather   _____
13. A line of people   _____
14. Rubber ring used in games   _____
15. A question   _____

Mammals

elephant giraffe porcupine camel
rhinoceros kangaroo polar bear
whale chimpanzee weasel

1. _____
2. _____
3. _____
4. _____
5. _____

6. _____
7. _____
8. _____
9. _____
10. _____

Score

ies

hurries   cities   gypsies   families   groceries
worries   armies   poppies   countries   strawberries

1. Sweet red fruits   _____

2. A wandering people   _____

3. Red flowers   _____

4. Nations   _____

5. Large bands of soldiers   _____

6. Troubles   _____

7. Very large towns   _____

8. Foods from a supermarket   _____

9. Groups of people related to
   each other   _____

10. Moves quickly   _____

ough { bough   though   borough   plough   through

11. Tool for turning the soil   _____

12. Concorde goes — the sound
    barrier   _____

13. A word meaning a town   _____

14. A branch of a tree   _____

15. He didn't cry even — it was
    painful   _____

16

ff

> offend   buffalo   different   sufficient
> shuffle   cuff   difficult   chauffeur   chaffinch

1. At the end of a sleeve _____

2. Not easy _____

3. Not the same _____

4. To hurt a person's feelings _____

5. Person paid to drive someone else _____

6. A kind of ox _____

7. Enough _____

8. To trail the feet _____

9. Small bird with pink breast _____

ex { examine   exercise   exciting   exhaust   exact   exaggerate

10. To make things seem better or worse than they are _____

11. Accurate _____

12. To look at carefully _____

13. Walking is very good — _____

14. Our car has a damaged — pipe _____

15. Thrilling _____

17

nn {
cannibal   annoyed   innocent   announcer

cannon   Kenneth   Channel   penniless

1. Introduces programmes on TV and radio   _____

2. Teased   _____

3. Without any money   _____

4. A boy's name   _____

5. A heavy gun   _____

6. Not guilty   _____

7. Eats human flesh   _____

8. Jersey is one of the — Islands   _____

cei

---

receive   deceit   perceive

deceive   ceiling   receipt   conceited

---

9. Thinking too highly of oneself   _____

10. The top of a room   _____

11. Trickery   _____

12. To accept   _____

13. To see and understand   _____

14. Piece of paper saying you have paid a sum of money.   _____

15. Those lies did not — her mother   _____

18

ea

leather	pleasure	treasure	Heather	instead
feathers	jealousy	deafening	threatened	
stealthily				

1. Pirates often buried it   _____
2. Philip went — of his brother   _____
3. Very noisy   _____
4. Made from animal skin   _____
5. Envy   _____
6. His father — to stop his pocket-money   _____
7. They cover a bird   _____
8. The old man crept — down the stairs   _____
9. A girl's name   _____
10. Delight   _____

or
{
conductor   inventor   tutor

seniors   sculptor
}

11. He carves in stone, wood, etc.   _____
12. A private teacher   _____
13. Older children   _____
14. One who invents   _____
15. Conducts an orchestra   _____

Building a skateboard

handsaw   hammer   screwdriver
wheels   skateboard   helmet   glove
knee pad   elbow pad   mallet

1. _____   6. _____
2. _____   7. _____
3. _____   8. _____
4. _____   9. _____
5. _____   10. _____

Score

Tricky Ones

I'm   don't   shan't   she's   they've
we'd   hasn't   they're   I'd   haven't
who's   that's   we're   you've   there'll

1. do not _____
2. she is _____
3. they are _____
4. have not _____
5. I would _____
6. who is _____
7. I am _____
8. we are _____
9. there will _____
10. has not _____
11. you have _____
12. shall not _____
13. we would _____
14. they have _____
15. that is _____

surprise	surface	survivor	surname	surveyor
surgeon	surgery	surely	surplice	surrounded

1. A doctor who operates _____

2. Something unexpected _____

3. Without doubt _____

4. A doctor's consulting room _____

5. White robe worn in church by clergy and choir _____

6. One who escapes with his life _____

7. Your family name _____

8. The top _____

9. Cut off on all sides _____

10. One who draws plans of land _____

rh {
  rhyme
  rhododendron
  rheumatism
  rhubarb
  rhinoceros
}

11. A plant with edible stalks _____

12. Words sounding alike are said to — _____

13. A painful disease _____

14. A beautiful shrub _____

15. Large animal with one or two horns _____

Peoples

> Australians   Spaniards   Belgians   Norwegians   Dutch
> Portuguese   Egyptians   Japanese   Hungarians   Turks

1.   Turkey   _____
2.   Japan   _____
3.   Egypt   _____
4.   Norway   _____
5.   Australia   _____

The people of

6.   Portugal   _____
7.   Belgium   _____
8.   Spain   _____
9.   Hungary   _____
10.   Holland   _____

cc { tobacconist   accordion   accept   buccaneer   success

11.   A pirate   _____
12.   To take what is offered   _____
13.   His new play was a huge —   _____
14.   He sells cigarettes   _____
15.   A musical instrument   _____

Occupations

confectioner gardener engineer stationer detective
ironmonger secretary fruiterer jeweller journalist

1. Sells pots, pans, nails, etc. _____

2. Sells fruit _____

3. Policeman in plain clothes _____

4. Writes letters for a person
   or firm _____

5. Sells writing paper, pens,
   etc. _____

6. Sells sweets, cakes, etc. _____

7. Writes articles for papers _____

8. Understands engines _____

9. Sells jewels, watches, etc. _____

10. He takes care of gardens _____

sc { scimitar   scissors
        scientist   scythe   sceptre

11. A household tool for cutting _____

12. A short curved sword _____

13. A rod held by a king _____

14. One who studies science _____

15. A tool for mowing long grass _____

On the skyline

church spire   lighthouse   windmill   pylon
castle ruins   lightning   tall chimney
dome   high-rise flats   mountain peak

1. _____   6. _____
2. _____   7. _____
3. _____   8. _____
4. _____   9. _____
5. _____   10. _____

Score

Buildings

hangar   museum   marquee   university   cathedral
theatre   library   factory   bungalow   monastery
garage   granary   abattoir   restaurant   skyscrapers

1. Built for a car _____

2. Plays are produced here _____

3. A one-storey house _____

4. For aeroplanes _____

5. A house for monks _____

6. You go here for a meal _____

7. A building for housing books _____

8. Interesting objects are on show here _____

9. For producing goods _____

10. Place of learning which awards degrees _____

11. New York is famous for these tall buildings _____

12. A very big church _____

13. A large tent _____

14. For storing grain _____

15. A slaughterhouse _____

foliage	viaduct	diagonal	financial	immediately
valiant	diamond	diameter	civilians	parliament

1. Leaves _____

2. Those who are not in the armed forces _____

3. Straightaway _____

4. A bridge _____

5. Precious stone _____

6. The line joining opposite corners of a rectangle _____

7. The line passing through the centre of a circle _____

8. Our laws are made by this body _____

9. To do with money _____

10. Bold _____

fied { dignified   satisfied   defied   crucified   magnified

11. Made greater _____

12. Executed on a cross _____

13. Stately _____

14. Contented _____

15. Resisted _____

gg

luggage   suggest   staggered
maggot   begging   leggings   toboggan

1. Clothing for the legs

2. Asking for money

3. The drunken man — from side
   to side

4. A sledge

5. Suitcases and trunks

6. To put forward an idea

7. A grub or caterpillar

il

until   tonsil   lentil   council
fulfil   stencil   utensil   daffodil

8. A body of men and women

9. To complete one's duties

10. A part of the throat

11. Yellow flower grown from
    a bulb

12. He waited — it was dark

13. A cut-out shape

14. A pan is a cooking —

15. A seed put in soup

ying

worrying   hurrying   bullying   copying   drying
carrying   replying   burying   denying   pitying

1. Bearing   _____

2. Answering   _____

3. Having pity   _____

4. Anxious   _____

5. Hitting a smaller person   _____

6. Covering with earth   _____

7. Going quickly   _____

8. Doing without something   _____

9. Making dry   _____

10. Making a copy   _____

exc   except   excel   excitement   exceedingly   excellent

11. It was — kind of you   _____

12. Very good indeed, perfect   _____

13. There was great — at the end of the race   _____

14. To do something well is to — at it   _____

15. The shop is open every day — Monday   _____

Fire!

fire engine   factory   hose   firemen
ambulance   spectators   casualty
dense smoke   fierce flames   policeman

1. _____
2. _____
3. _____
4. _____
5. _____

6. _____
7. _____
8. _____
9. _____
10. _____

Score

30

miraculous	mischievous	hideous	unanimous
	monotonous	miscellaneous	
courageous	humorous	generous	anonymous

1. Ugly   _____

2. Funny   _____

3. Gives to others readily   _____

4. Brave   _____

5. Dull   _____

6. When all are in agreement   _____

7. Very wonderful   _____

8. Name not known   _____

9. Full of mischief   _____

10. Assorted   _____

fore { foremost   forecast   forearm   forehead   foreman

11. Front part of the head   _____

12. From the wrist to the elbow   _____

13. Look into the future   _____

14. A man in charge of other workmen   _____

15. Outstanding   _____

ful

> merciful   colourful   dreadful
> grateful   tasteful   careful   painful

1. Having mercy   _____
2. Awful   _____
3. Hurting   _____
4. In good taste   _____
5. Opposite of careless   _____
6. Gives thanks willingly   _____
7. With plenty of colour   _____

fully { painfully   dolefully   faithfully   beautifully   cheerfully   carefully   lawfully   truthfully }

8. Merrily   _____
9. To reduce accidents motorists must drive —   _____
10. With pain   _____
11. Miserably   _____
12. Another word for loyally   _____
13. Honestly   _____
14. Keeping within the law   _____
15. With great beauty   _____

our

vigour saviour splendour favourite harbour
honour contour behaviour armoured courteous

1. All promised to be on their best — _____

2. Strength of body _____

3. Place of shelter for ships _____

4. Magnificence and brilliance _____

5. Polite _____

6. One who saves another _____

7. Protected by thick metal _____

8. To be knighted is a great — _____

9. My — colour is blue _____

10. A line on a map showing height _____

pp { appetite appalling application apprentice apparatus

11. As he had no — the sick man left his food _____

12. A youngster who is learning the trade _____

13. A word meaning equipment _____

14. Dreadful _____

15. A request (often sent when seeking a job) _____

33

stirring	currants	terrier	tomorrow
surrender	correction	Mediterranean	
barracks	irritate	terrific	torrent

1. Sea between Europe and Africa _____

2. Soldiers live in these _____

3. To give in _____

4. A small dog _____

5. Mum said, 'Keep — the gravy' _____

6. Dried grapes _____

7. A putting right of something wrong _____

8. If you annoy a person you — him _____

9. A — of water rushed down the valley _____

10. The day after today _____

11. The car went at — speed _____

mn { solemn   autumn   column   condemn

12. A sort of pillar often supporting the roof of a building _____

13. Third season of our year _____

14. To blame _____

15. A word meaning serious _____

34

At the railway station

ticket-collector   porter   suitcases
briefcase   tennis-racket   spaniel
clock   bookstall   advertisement   barrier

1. _____
2. _____
3. _____
4. _____
5. _____
6. _____
7. _____
8. _____
9. _____
10. _____

Score

ial

---

artificial   material   aerial   perennial   essential

---

1. A plant which comes up year after year   _____

2. Sends or receives a radio signal   _____

3. Necessary   _____

4. Not natural   _____

5. Another word for cloth   _____

nn { running grinning winning planning beginning tinned skinned pinned planned sun-tanned

6. Leading in a race   _____

7. Going fast   _____

8. Starting   _____

9. Smiling broadly   _____

10. Making plans   _____

11. Fastened with a pin   _____

12. Made a plan   _____

13. Put into a tin   _____

14. Took off the skin   _____

15. Browned by the sun   _____

| Tricky ones | moustache Michael picnic persuade colonel |
| | parachute pageant khaki sergeant Margaret |

1. A means of escape from a plane _____

2. Soldier with three stripes _____

3. Light-brown cloth worn by the army _____

4. A girl's name _____

5. Hair on the upper lip _____

6. A display of historical figures _____

7. A boy's name _____

8. To bring round to your way of thinking _____

9. A meal out in the open air _____

10. The sergeant would salute this one _____

| eon | luncheon truncheon |
| | pigeon dungeon galleon |

11. Bird often trained to carry messages _____

12. An underground cell _____

13. A meal _____

14. Spanish sailing ship _____

15. A sort of heavy stick _____

wh

whist   whistle   whiskers   whether   Whitsuntide
wharf   whisky   whimper   whispered   whooping-cough

1. A beard is made up of these   _____
2. A card game   _____
3. A disease   _____
4. A musical instrument   _____
5. Spoke very softly   _____
6. A riverside quay   _____
7. A drink   _____
8. A pitiful cry   _____
9. A church festival   _____
10. If   _____

ou { poultry   mould   shoulder   smoulder   boulder

11. A rock   _____
12. Where the arm joins the body   _____
13. To burn slowly   _____
14. Chickens, ducks, geese, etc.   _____
15. Found growing in damp places   _____

38

de

decide　describe　destroyed
despair　descend　democracy　detergent

1. To go down _____
2. Cleaning liquid or powder _____
3. To give up hope _____
4. To make up one's mind _____
5. To give details of _____
6. Government by the people _____
7. Demolished _____

ty

forty　majority　eighty　honesty
safety　velocity　ninety　novelty

8. 80 _____
9. Most of those present _____
10. A new idea or thing _____
11. 40 _____
12. 90 _____
13. Truthfulness _____
14. The injured climber was
    hauled to — _____
15. Speed _____

Fast movers

Concorde   racing car   swallow   athlete
rocket   clipper   motor cycle
peregrine   train   hare

1. _____   6. _____
2. _____   7. _____
3. _____   8. _____
4. _____   9. _____
5. _____   10. _____

Score

40

ar

```
jaguar    Cheddar   peculiar   dollar   separate
scholar   poplar    popular    vulgar   caterpillars
```

1. American animal like a tiger   _____

2. Queer, strange   _____

3. American money   _____

4. Rude   _____

5. A pupil   _____

6. Come from the eggs of
   butterflies and moths   _____

7. A type of cheese   _____

8. A tree   _____

9. Much liked   _____

10. Not joined together   _____

ll { collide   intelligence   rebellion
     quarrelled   signalled

11. Became unfriendly   _____

12. An uprising   _____

13. To bump into   _____

14. Cleverness of mind   _____

15. Gave a sign   _____

41

Famous Names

> Victoria   Trafalgar   Canterbury   Everest
> Tchaikovsky   Caesar   Gibraltar   Beethoven
> Elizabeth II   Pontius Pilate   Pyramids
> Australia   Churchill   Canberra   Himalayas

1. Our Queen   _____

2. A British prime minister   _____

3. A famous rock   _____

4. A queen who reigned for 64 years   _____

5. Where kangaroos and koala bears live   _____

6. A Roman who invaded Britain   _____

7. An English cathedral   _____

8. A Russian composer   _____

9. The Roman governor in Jerusalem at the time of Christ's crucifixion   _____

10. Ancient Egyptian tombs   _____

11. A famous naval battle   _____

12. Highest mountain in the world   _____

13. The capital of Australia   _____

14. This range of mountains contains Mount Everest   _____

15. A German composer   _____

o

potato   buffalo   mosquito
volcano   Negro   tomato   cargo

1. A kind of ox   _____
2. Vesuvius is a —   _____
3. A red fruit   _____
4. A starchy food   _____
5. The goods carried by a ship   _____
6. An insect   _____
7. A member of an African race   _____

oes { echoes   buffaloes   mosquitoes   potatoes   tomatoes   Negroes   volcanoes   dominoes }

8. Insects   _____
9. The plural of potato   _____
10. Ox-like animals   _____
11. The plural of Negro   _____
12. Mountains which erupt   _____
13. Plural of tomato   _____
14. Reflected sounds   _____
15. A game   _____

e + ing

aching	exciting	surprising	sparkling	escaping
dining	driving	examining	believing	perspiring
losing	refusing	smuggling	rejoicing	underlining

1. Hurting   _____

2. Thrilling   _____

3. Evading paying customs-duty   _____

4. Having a belief   _____

5. Saying 'no'   _____

6. Drawing lines under   _____

7. Eating dinner   _____

8. Controlling a car   _____

9. Glittering   _____

10. Fleeing   _____

11. Inspecting   _____

12. Opposite of winning   _____

13. Being joyful   _____

14. Sweating   _____

15. Astonishing   _____

Birds

stork   mallard   swallow   pigeon
pheasant   parrot   peacock
sparrow   eagle   budgerigar

1. _____
2. _____
3. _____
4. _____
5. _____

6. _____
7. _____
8. _____
9. _____
10. _____

Score

ly

usually   generously   dangerously
seriously   thoroughly   vertically   miserably

1. In a dangerous manner   _____
2. At right angles to the horizon   _____
3. In a serious manner   _____
4. Sadly   _____
5. Not meanly   _____
6. Completely   _____
7. Generally   _____

ly {
wisely   sincerely   accurately   delicately
lovely   strangely   separately   immediately
}

8. One at a time   _____
9. Daintily   _____
10. Beautiful   _____
11. In a sincere manner   _____
12. In a wise manner   _____
13. In a strange manner   _____
14. Correctly   _____
15. At once   _____

tyre dynamo dynamite plywood typewriter
pylon thyme hygiene hydrogen hyacinths
tyrant python dynamic cyclone hydro-electricity

1. Electricity made by
   water-power   _____

2. Rubber part of a car wheel   _____

3. A large snake   _____

4. A garden herb   _____

5. High winds   _____

6. They will flower indoors in
   winter   _____

7. Metal tower to carry power
   lines   _____

8. Dictator   _____

9. To do with cleanliness   _____

10. Board made from thin layers
    of wood   _____

11. Used for causing explosions   _____

12. A light gas   _____

13. A secretary uses a —   _____

14. Machine for making electric
    current   _____

15. Energetic   _____

Shopping List

celery	mayonnaise	biscuits	lettuce	marmalade
yogurt	cauliflower	currants	cereals	chocolate
salmon	raspberries	walnuts	sausages	margarine

1. Green leaves eaten in salads   _____

2. A dressing used on salads   _____

3. Usually put into skins   _____

4. Made from milk   _____

5. Nuts   _____

6. Made from cacao seeds   _____

7. A fish   _____

8. Used like butter   _____

9. Crisp food often eaten with a cup of tea   _____

10. Grain we eat   _____

11. A long-stemmed vegetable   _____

12. Made with oranges and sugar   _____

13. Like a cabbage with a white head   _____

14. A red fruit   _____

15. Dried fruit   _____

sses {
addresses   mattresses   compasses   bypasses

air-hostesses   princesses

witnesses   businesses   actresses   expresses
}

1. Very fast trains   _____

2. Daughters of kings and queens   _____

3. Those who see an event   _____

4. The fire destroyed both beds and —   _____

5. Firms engaged in buying and selling   _____

6. Roads taking heavy traffic away from cities   _____

7. Used for finding direction   _____

8. This club is used by famous actors and —   _____

9. The policeman took our names and —   _____

10. They attend to the needs of aircraft passengers   _____

pp {
kidnapping   dropping   flapping

whipping   worshipping
}

11. Flogging   _____

12. Fluttering of wings   _____

13. Stealing a person   _____

14. Letting fall   _____

15. Offering praise to God   _____

At the hospital

doctor   stethoscope   nurse   trolley
sling   plaster-leg   magazine
scissors   wheelchair   bandages

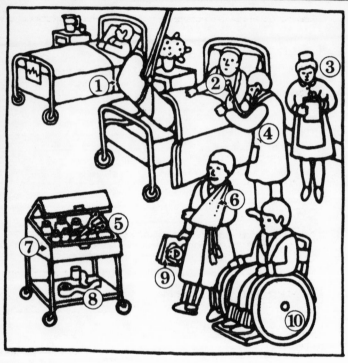

1. _____
2. _____
3. _____
4. _____
5. _____

6. _____
7. _____
8. _____
9. _____
10. _____

Score

listened   tunnelled   happened   uncovered
disappeared   coloured   murdered   conquered
unfastened   surrendered   borrowed   addressed
armoured   whispered   frightened

1. Gave up the struggle   _____

2. Heard   _____

3. The Roman army — much of the known world   _____

4. Burrowed underground   _____

5. Possessing colour   _____

6. Took a person's life   _____

7. Vanished   _____

8. The officer climbed into his — car   _____

9. The passengers — their seat belts   _____

10. John returned the library books he had —   _____

11. Took place   _____

12. Took off the cover   _____

13. Afraid   _____

14. The envelope was — quite clearly   _____

15. Spoke in a very gentle voice   _____

> battery   brewery   machinery   millinery
> stationery   mystery   cemetery   jewellery
> artillery   confectionery

1. Electricity is stored in a —   _____

2. The reason for the crime remained a —   _____

3. Where beer is made   _____

4. Department for women's hats   _____

5. Guns   _____

6. Engineers are overhauling the —   _____

7. Cakes, pastries, etc.   _____

8. A burial place   _____

9. Diamonds and emeralds are types of —   _____

10. Writing-paper, etc.   _____

gue ⎰ colleague   rogue   league
    ⎱ intrigue   catalogue

11. Booklet containing a list   _____

12. Scoundrel   _____

13. Secret plotting   _____

14. A table of teams   _____

15. A friend   _____

cious {
spacious   delicious   unconscious   vicious

precious   atrocious   suspicious
}

1. Valuable   _____

2. A blow on the head can make you this   _____

3. Awful   _____

4. Pleasant to eat   _____

5. Spiteful   _____

6. Distrustful   _____

7. With lots of room   _____

gn {
gnashed   gnomon   gnome

gnarled
}

8. A goblin   _____

9. The rod on a sundial which casts the shadow   _____

10. Knotted and twisted   _____

11. The man — his teeth in anger   _____

tious {
superstitious   infectious

conscientious   cautious
}

12. Always does his best   _____

13. Measles is an — disease   _____

14. Wary   _____

15. He was — and never walked under ladders   _____

ar

> lunar   vinegar   circular   particulars
> regular   similar   calendar   perpendicular
> nuclear   burglar   muscular

1. A housebreaker　　　　　　_____
2. To do with atoms　　　　　_____
3. Round　　　　　　　　　　_____
4. A list of days and months　_____
5. A sour liquid　　　　　　　_____
6. Upright　　　　　　　　　　_____
7. Alike　　　　　　　　　　　_____
8. Evenly spaced　　　　　　　_____
9. Detail　　　　　　　　　　　_____
10. To do with the moon　　　　_____
11. Brawny, strong　　　　　　_____

Using 'un' { unnoticed   unnecessary   unnatural   unneighbourly

12. Not necessary　　　　　　_____
13. Not noticed　　　　　　　_____
14. Not neighbourly　　　　　_____
15. Not natural　　　　　　　_____

54

Boating

dinghy   mast   pennant
life-jacket   rowing boat   mainsail
oars   buoy   jib   tiller

1. _____   6. _____
2. _____   7. _____
3. _____   8. _____
4. _____   9. _____
5. _____   10. _____

Score

ll

overall   lollipop   bulldozer   caterpillar
millimetres   woollen   jeweller   swollen
jewellery   illustration   parallel   plimsolls
penicillin   millionaire   cellophane

1. 1000 make a metre   _____

2. He sells precious stones   _____

3. Used in the cure of disease   _____

4. Light shoes   _____

5. Railway lines are — to each
   other   _____

6. A very rich man   _____

7. A sweet   _____

8. Machine for moving earth   _____

9. Protective clothing   _____

10. Transparent wrapping material   _____

11. Grub which changes into a
    butterfly   _____

12. Made of wool   _____

13. A picture   _____

14. My finger is — from the
    bee sting   _____

15. Precious stones, gold rings, etc.   _____

ture

torture   capture   scripture   puncture

temperature   manufacture   architecture

lecture   overture   furniture   literature

1. To inflict pain   _____
2. To make   _____
3. A talk given to a class   _____
4. A hole in a tyre   _____
5. Tables, chairs, etc.   _____
6. An introductory piece of
   music   _____
7. To make prisoner   _____
8. The writings of a country   _____
9. The study of building   _____
10. Degree of hotness   _____
11. Sacred writings   _____

aero { aerodrome   aerosol   aerobatics   aeroplane

12. An aircraft   _____
13. A spray   _____
14. A display of clever flying   _____
15. Where aircraft land   _____

meter

> thermometer   ammeter   barometer
> voltmeter   altimeter   speedometer

1. For measuring electric current   _____

2. For measuring air pressure   _____

3. For measuring speed   _____

4. For measuring height   _____

5. For measuring heat   _____

6. For measuring electric voltage   _____

acc
> accent   accessory
> accidents   accept   accelerate

7. I shall be pleased to — your invitation   _____

8. An additional part   _____

9. Increase speed   _____

10. Our visitor speaks English with a French —   _____

11. In fog drivers must guard against —   _____

metre
> metre   centimetre   millimetre   kilometre

12. 1/1000th part of a metre   _____

13. 10 millimetres = 1 —   _____

14. 100 centimetres = 1 —   _____

15. 1000 metres = 1 —   _____

58

ch

christen   chasm   Christmas   chiropodist
chlorine   chronicle   chemistry   Christianity
chrysalis   chorister   chromium   chrysanthemum

1. A flower   _____

2. The study of chemicals   _____

3. A gas   _____

4. When the birth of Jesus
   Christ is celebrated   _____

5. A stage in the life of an insect   _____

6. One who treats feet   _____

7. A deep home   _____

8. The Christian faith   _____

9. To give a name to   _____

10. A list of events   _____

11. A metal   _____

12. A member of a choir   _____

que {   grotesque   cheque
              picturesque

13. Beautiful   _____

14. He wrote a — for the money
    he owed   _____

15. Ugly   _____

59

The Collision

diesel-electric locomotive   level-crossing   tunnel
tank-wagon   viaduct   station   rails
signal box   brake-van   buffer-stop

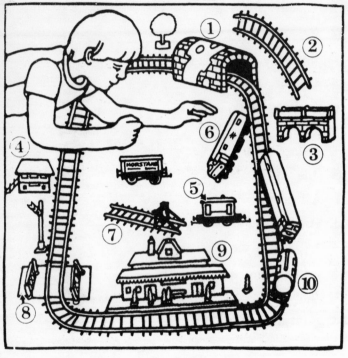

1. _____   6. _____
2. _____   7. _____
3. _____   8. _____
4. _____   9. _____
5. _____   10. _____

Score

att

attic   attempt   attitude
attack   attached   attractive   attendant

1. Assault   _____

2. Beautiful   _____

3. Strive   _____

4. He — a rope to the car   _____

5. At the petrol pump there
   was no —   _____

6. A room near to the roof of
   a house   _____

7. Manner   _____

Using 'un' { unusual   unequal   unemployed   unaffected
unofficial   unintelligible   unaccompanied
unknown }

8. Cannot be understood   _____

9. Without work   _____

10. Not equal   _____

11. Not affected by   _____

12. Out of the ordinary   _____

13. Alone   _____

14. Not confirmed by an official   _____

15. Not known   _____

oar

| boarder | coarse | hoard | cupboard | hoarse |

1. For storing things in _____

2. To save _____

3. Rough _____

4. A husky voice is said to be — _____

5. A boy or girl at boarding-school _____

al { almost already although
     almighty always }

6. All powerful _____

7. It was cold — it was sunny _____

8. Forever _____

9. Nearly _____

10. When the alarm was raised the building was — blazing _____

irr { irregular irreligious irrigation
      irresponsible irritable }

11. Not responsible _____

12. A method of watering crops _____

13. Bad-tempered _____

14. Not regular _____

15. Not religious _____

62

Pursuits

athletics	philately	gymnastics	skin-diving
mountaineering	karate	yachting	electronics
archaeology	ornithology	antiques	pot-holing
astronomy	photography	amateur dramatics	

1. The study of birds   _____

2. Using a camera   _____

3. The study of the stars   _____

4. Unpaid acting   _____

5. Study of ancient remains   _____

6. Stamp collecting   _____

7. Sailing   _____

8. A gymnasium is the proper place for these   _____

9. Running, jumping, hurdling, etc.   _____

10. He was a collector of —   _____

11. A type of unarmed combat   _____

12. Climbing mountains   _____

13. Exploring underground passages   _____

14. Underwater swimming   _____

15. His knowledge of — helped him to repair the radio   _____

(1)	(2)	(3)
1. piece	1. wrapper	1. jewel
2. grieve	2. wreckage	2. barrel
3. believe	3. writhe	3. shovel
4. niece	4. wrong	4. camel
5. shield	5. wrath	5. funnel
6. chief	6. wretched	6. tunnel
7. yield	7. wrestling	7. panel
8. field	8. wren	8. gospel
9. pierce	9. wrist-watch	9. flannel
10. fierce	10. wreath	10. quarrel
11. thief	11. fudge	11. mortar
12. priest	12. hedgehog	12. collar
13. mischief	13. hedge	13. sugar
14. handkerchief	14. bridge	14. beggar
15. siege	15. sledge	15. cellar

(4)	(5)	(6)
1. weigh	1. spectators	1. autumn
2. reign	2. balcony	2. author
3. foreign	3. spring-board	3. gaudy
4. eight	4. whistle	4. saunter
5. seize	5. goggles	5. laundry
6. weight	6. towel	6. sauce
7. their	7. swimming	7. saucer
8. neighbour	instructor	8. vault
9. rein	8. handrail	9. haul
10. weird	9. swimsuit	10. saucepan
11. neither	10. flippers	11. sausages
12. neigh		12. draught
13. neighbourhood		13. autograph
14. heifer		14. August
15. height		15. mauve

(7)

1. cottage
2. butterfly
3. bottom
4. gutter
5. button
6. jersey
7. valley
8. spinney
9. parsley
10. barley
11. journey
12. Geoffrey
13. turkey
14. obeyed
15. disobeyed

(8)

1. terrifying
2. hyphen
3. lying
4. magnifying
5. rhyme
6. typist
7. dying
8. dyeing
9. rhythm
10. poetry
11. bury
12. berry
13. syrup
14. enemy
15. symphony

(9)

1. poisons
2. coiled
3. oilfield
4. rejoice
5. boiling
6. joint
7. loiter
8. voice
9. ointment
10. psalms
11. palm
12. yolk
13. chalk
14. calm
15. folk

(10)

1. parachutist
2. plough
3. gypsy caravan
4. cattle
5. donkey
6. invalid
7. worm
8. hedgehog
9. tortoise
10. snail

(11)

1. wedding
2. middle
3. pudding
4. address
5. saddle
6. hidden
7. suddenly
8. nodding
9. midday
10. ladder
11. ribbon
12. grabbed
13. cabbage
14. rubbish
15. scribble

(12)

1. position
2. election
3. dictionary
4. motion
5. decoration
6. station
7. invention
8. correction
9. ration
10. protection
11. jealous
12. nervous
13. famous
14. enormous
15. poisonous

(13)
1. assistant
2. business
3. assembly
4. pressure
5. passport
6. possess
7. Swiss
8. message
9. passengers
10. necessary
11. pheasant
12. orphan
13. phantom
14. triumph
15. photograph

(14)
1. murder
2. turban
3. murmur
4. turquoise
5. pursue
6. figure
7. purpose
8. furniture
9. conquer
10. conqueror
11. quantity
12. quill
13. queue
14. quoit
15. query

(15)
1. polar bear
2. whale
3. rhinoceros
4. kangaroo
5. porcupine
6. giraffe
7. chimpanzee
8. camel
9. weasel
10. elephant

(16)
1. strawberries
2. gypsies
3. poppies
4. countries
5. armies
6. worries
7. cities
8. groceries
9. families
10. hurries
11. plough
12. through
13. borough
14. bough
15. though

(17)
1. cuff
2. difficult
3. different
4. offend
5. chauffeur
6. buffalo
7. sufficient
8. shuffle
9. chaffinch
10. exaggerate
11. exact
12. examine
13. exercise
14. exhaust
15. exciting

(18)
1. announcer
2. annoyed
3. penniless
4. Kenneth
5. cannon
6. innocent
7. cannibal
8. Channel
9. conceited
10. ceiling
11. deceit
12. receive
13. perceive
14. receipt
15. deceive

(19)
1. treasure
2. instead
3. deafening
4. leather
5. jealousy
6. threatened
7. feathers
8. stealthily
9. Heather
10. pleasure
11. sculptor
12. tutor
13. seniors
14. inventor
15. conductor

(20)
1. screwdriver
2. handsaw
3. mallet
4. helmet
5. hammer
6. glove
7. elbow pad
8. knee pad
9. wheels
10. skateboard

(21)
1. don't
2. she's
3. they're
4. haven't
5. I'd
6. who's
7. I'm
8. we're
9. there'll
10. hasn't
11. you've
12. shan't
13. we'd
14. they've
15. that's

(22)
1. surgeon
2. surprise
3. surely
4. surgery
5. surplice
6. survivor
7. surname
8. surface
9. surrounded
10. surveyor
11. rhubarb
12. rhyme
13. rheumatism
14. rhododendron
15. rhinoceros

(23)
1. Turks
2. Japanese
3. Egyptians
4. Norwegians
5. Australians
6. Portuguese
7. Belgians
8. Spaniards
9. Hungarians
10. Dutch
11. buccaneer
12. accept
13. success
14. tobacconist
15. accordion

(24)
1. ironmonger
2. fruiterer
3. detective
4. secretary
5. stationer
6. confectioner
7. journalist
8. engineer
9. jeweller
10. gardener
11. scissors
12. scimitar
13. sceptre
14. scientist
15. scythe

(25)
1. castle ruins
2. lighthouse
3. lightning
4. mountain peak
5. pylon
6. windmill
7. church spire
8. tall chimney
9. dome
10. high-rise flats

(26)
1. garage
2. theatre
3. bungalow
4. hangar
5. monastery
6. restaurant
7. library
8. museum
9. factory
10. university
11. skyscrapers
12. cathedral
13. marquee
14. granary
15. abattoir

(27)
1. foliage
2. civilians
3. immediately
4. viaduct
5. diamond
6. diagonal
7. diameter
8. parliament
9. financial
10. valiant
11. magnified
12. crucified
13. dignified
14. satisfied
15. defied

(28)
1. leggings
2. begging
3. staggered
4. toboggan
5. luggage
6. suggest
7. maggot
8. council
9. fulfil
10. tonsil
11. daffodil
12. until
13. stencil
14. utensil
15. lentil

(29)
1. carrying
2. replying
3. pitying
4. worrying
5. bullying
6. burying
7. hurrying
8. denying
9. drying
10. copying
11. exceedingly
12. excellent
13. excitement
14. excel
15. except

(30)
1. factory
2. dense smoke
3. fierce flames
4. fire engine
5. hose
6. firemen
7. ambulance
8. spectators
9. policeman
10. casualty

(31)
1. hideous
2. humorous
3. generous
4. courageous
5. monotonous
6. unanimous
7. miraculous
8. anonymous
9. mischievous
10. miscellaneous
11. forehead
12. forearm
13. forecast
14. foreman
15. foremost

(32)
1. merciful
2. dreadful
3. painful
4. tasteful
5. careful
6. grateful
7. colourful
8. cheerfully
9. carefully
10. painfully
11. dolefully
12. faithfully
13. truthfully
14. lawfully
15. beautifully

(33)
1. behaviour
2. vigour
3. harbour
4. splendour
5. courteous
6. saviour
7. armoured
8. honour
9. favourite
10. contour
11. appetite
12. apprentice
13. apparatus
14. appalling
15. application

(34)
1. Mediterranean
2. barracks
3. surrender
4. terrier
5. stirring
6. currants
7. correction
8. irritate
9. torrent
10. tomorrow
11. terrific
12. column
13. autumn
14. condemn
15. solemn

(35)
1. advertisement
2. clock
3. bookstall
4. barrier
5. porter
6. ticket-collector
7. tennis-racket
8. briefcase
9. spaniel
10. suitcases

(36)
1. perennial
2. aerial
3. essential
4. artificial
5. material
6. winning
7. running
8. beginning
9. grinning
10. planning
11. pinned
12. planned
13. tinned
14. skinned
15. sun-tanned

(37)
1. parachute
2. sergeant
3. khaki
4. Margaret
5. moustache
6. pageant
7. Michael
8. persuade
9. picnic
10. colonel
11. pigeon
12. dungeon
13. luncheon
14. galleon
15. truncheon

(38)
1. whiskers
2. whist
3. whooping-cough
4. whistle
5. whispered
6. wharf
7. whisky
8. whimper
9. Whitsuntide
10. whether
11. boulder
12. shoulder
13. smoulder
14. poultry
15. mould

(39)
1. descend
2. detergent
3. despair
4. decide
5. describe
6. democracy
7. destroyed
8. eighty
9. majority
10. novelty
11. forty
12. ninety
13. honesty
14. safety
15. velocity

(40)
1. rocket
2. Concorde
3. swallow
4. clipper
5. peregrine
6. train
7. racing car
8. motor cycle
9. hare
10. athlete

(41)
1. jaguar
2. peculiar
3. dollar
4. vulgar
5. scholar
6. caterpillars
7. Cheddar
8. poplar
9. popular
10. separate
11. quarrelled
12. rebellion
13. collide
14. intelligence
15. signalled

(42)
1. Elizabeth II
2. Churchill
3. Gibraltar
4. Victoria
5. Australia
6. Caesar
7. Canterbury
8. Tchaikovsky
9. Pontius Pilate
10. Pyramids
11. Trafalgar
12. Everest
13. Canberra
14. Himalayas
15. Beethoven

(43)
1. buffalo
2. volcano
3. tomato
4. potato
5. cargo
6. mosquito
7. Negro
8. mosquitoes
9. potatoes
10. buffaloes
11. Negroes
12. volcanoes
13. tomatoes
14. echoes
15. dominoes

(44)
1. aching
2. exciting
3. smuggling
4. believing
5. refusing
6. underlining
7. dining
8. driving
9. sparkling
10. escaping
11. examining
12. losing
13. rejoicing
14. perspiring
15. surprising

(45)
1. swallow
2. eagle
3. parrot
4. peacock
5. stork
6. budgerigar
7. sparrow
8. mallard
9. pheasant
10. pigeon

(46)
1. dangerously
2. vertically
3. seriously
4. miserably
5. generously
6. thoroughly
7. usually
8. separately
9. delicately
10. lovely
11. sincerely
12. wisely
13. strangely
14. accurately
15. immediately

(47)
1. hydro-electricity
2. tyre
3. python
4. thyme
5. cyclone
6. hyacinths
7. pylon
8. tyrant
9. hygiene
10. plywood
11. dynamite
12. hydrogen
13. typewriter
14. dynamo
15. dynamic

(48)
1. lettuce
2. mayonnaise
3. sausages
4. yogurt
5. walnuts
6. chocolate
7. salmon
8. margarine
9. biscuits
10. cereals
11. celery
12. marmalade
13. cauliflower
14. raspberries
15. currants

(49)
1. expresses
2. princesses
3. witnesses
4. mattresses
5. businesses
6. bypasses
7. compasses
8. actresses
9. addresses
10. air-hostesses
11. whipping
12. flapping
13. kidnapping
14. dropping
15. worshipping

(50)
1. plaster-leg
2. stethoscope
3. nurse
4. doctor
5. scissors
6. sling
7. trolley
8. bandages
9. magazine
10. wheelchair

(51)
1. surrendered
2. listened
3. conquered
4. tunnelled
5. coloured
6. murdered
7. disappeared
8. armoured
9. unfastened
10. borrowed
11. happened
12. uncovered
13. frightened
14. addressed
15. whispered

(52)
1. battery
2. mystery
3. brewery
4. millinery
5. artillery
6. machinery
7. confectionery
8. cemetery
9. jewellery
10. stationery
11. catalogue
12. rogue
13. intrigue
14. league
15. colleague ·

(53)
1. precious
2. unconscious
3. atrocious
4. delicious
5. vicious
6. suspicious
7. spacious
8. gnome
9. gnomon
10. gnarled
11. gnashed
12. conscientious
13. infectious
14. cautious
15. superstitious

(54)
1. burglar
2. nuclear
3. circular
4. calendar
5. vinegar
6. perpendicular
7. similar
8. regular
9. particulars
10. lunar
11. muscular
12. unnecessary
13. unnoticed
14. unneighbourly
15. unnatural

(55)
1. rowing boat
2. oars
3. pennant
4. buoy
5. mainsail
6. mast
7. jib
8. life-jacket
9. tiller
10. dinghy

(56)
1. millimetres
2. jeweller
3. penicillin
4. plimsolls
5. parallel
6. millionaire
7. lollipop
8. bulldozer
9. overall
10. cellophane
11. caterpillar
12. woollen
13. illustration
14. swollen
15. jewellery

(57)
1. torture
2. manufacture
3. lecture
4. puncture
5. furniture
6. overture
7. capture
8. literature
9. architecture
10. temperature
11. scripture
12. aeroplane
13. aerosol
14. aerobatics
15. aerodrome

(58)
1. ammeter
2. barometer
3. speedometer
4. altimeter
5. thermometer
6. voltmeter
7. accept
8. accessory
9. accelerate
10. accent
11. accidents
12. millimetre
13. centimetre
14. metre
15. kilometre

(59)
1. chrysanthemum
2. chemistry
3. chlorine
4. Christmas
5. chrysalis
6. chiropodist
7. chasm
8. Christianity
9. christen
10. chronicle
11. chromium
12. chorister
13. picturesque
14. cheque
15. grotesque

(60)
1. tunnel
2. rails
3. viaduct
4. signal box
5. brake-van
6. diesel-electric locomotive
7. buffer-stop
8. level-crossing
9. station
10. tank-wagon

(61)	(62)	(63)
1. attack	1. cupboard	1. ornithology
2. attractive	2. hoard	2. photography
3. attempt	3. coarse	3. astronomy
4. attached	4. hoarse	4. amateur dramatics
5. attendant	5. boarder	5. archaeology
6. attic	6. almighty	6. philately
7. attitude	7. although	7. yachting
8. unintelligible	8. always	8. gymnastics
9. unemployed	9. almost	9. athletics
10. unequal	10. already	10. antiques
11. unaffected	11. irresponsible	11. karate
12. unusual	12. irrigation	12. mountaineering
13. unaccompanied	13. irritable	13. pot-holing
14. unofficial	14. irregular	14. skin-diving
15. unknown	15. irreligious	15. electronics

Spelling
Quiz Book 3

CONTENTS

Cycling

tandem	tricycle	reflector	lubricate	mudguard
bicycle	dynamo	efficient	pneumatic	maintenance
enamel	puncture	accidents	milometer	tyre-lever

1. Red disc on rear of cycle _____
2. Prevents mud splashes _____
3. Air-filled tyres _____
4. A hole in the inner tube _____
5. Hard, shiny covering on the metal _____
6. A two-wheeled cycle _____
7. A three-wheeled cycle _____
8. Tool for removing a tyre _____
9. To oil _____
10. Check brakes to see they are — _____
11. Poor brakes may cause — _____
12. Cycle for two riders _____
13. It makes electricity _____
14. Records the distance travelled _____
15. Cleaning, oiling and repairing of a cycle _____

i before e — except after c	th--ves	sh--ld	n--ce	bel--ve	fr--nd
	c--ling	p--ce	pat--nt	rec--ve	dec--ve

1. Roof of a room _____

2. To have faith _____

3. A pal _____

4. Robbers _____

5. Looked after by a doctor _____

6. Protect _____

7. A part of something _____

8. Your brother's or sister's daughter _____

9. To cheat or mislead _____

10. Winners will — prizes _____

tt { knitted   trotted   batted   fitted   plotted

11. { fit _____

12. { trot _____

13. A word made from { knit _____

14. { plot _____

15. { bat _____

2

y + ily	easy sturdy tidy merry ordinary
	lucky
	ready unhappy angry sleepy

1. In a sturdy manner   _____

2. In the ordinary way   _____

3. Happily   _____

4. Simply   _____

5. Willingly   _____

6. In a sleepy manner   _____

7. Furiously   _____

8. Sadly   _____

9. Fortunately   _____

10. In a tidy manner   _____

*The acrostic would turn you head over heels

| Largest Islands | New Guinea   Malagasy Republic |
| | Borneo   Greenland   Australia |

11. Largest island; smallest
continent   _____

12. Second largest; partly
ice-covered   _____

13. North of Australia with dense
forests   _____

14. In East Indies and fourth
largest   _____

15. Off Africa; once called
Madagascar and fifth in size   _____

In the Kitchen

sieve	scissors	saucepan	detergent	cupboards
caddy	drawers	casserole	percolator	refrigerator
ladle	dessert	serrated	polythene	greaseproof

1. Washing-up liquid   _____

2. For storing tea   _____

3. A pan used for boiling   _____

4. Machine for keeping food cool   _____

5. Has tiny holes for straining   _____

6. Transparent material   _____

7. Storage places with doors   _____

8. Dish for cooking meats slowly   _____

9. Long-handled spoon for serving soup   _____

10. A cutting tool   _____

11. Paper for lining tins   _____

12. Used for making coffee   _____

13. Medium-sized spoon for sweets   _____

14. Sliding containers   _____

15. Breadknives have — edges   _____

Buildings

theatre   railway station   pyramid
detached house   semi-detached house   palace
hangar   skyscraper   factory   thatched cottage

1. _____   6. _____
2. _____   7. _____
3. _____   8. _____
4. _____   9. _____
5. _____   10. _____

Score

Measures { metre   kilometre   centimetre   kilogram   millimetre

1. mm   _____
2. m   _____
3. kg   _____
4. cm   _____
5. km   _____

ei { Neil   Sheila   Eiffel Tower   leisure   seize   foreigner

6. To grab   _____
7. Person from another country   _____
8. Free time   _____
9. A girl's name   _____
10. A boy's name   _____
11. In Paris and over 299m high   _____

meter { thermometer   altimeter   barometer   gasometer

12. Vessel for holding gas   _____
13. Instrument showing a plane's height   _____
14. Instrument for measuring heat   _____
15. Instrument for measuring air pressure   _____

6

Soccer

referee	substitute	television	international
amateur	decisions	spectators	ninety minutes
divisions	linesmen	professional	penalty kick
Football Association		centre-forward	goals

1. A player who is paid to play _____

2. A player who is not paid _____

3. The letters F.A. mean — _____

4. Middle player in the forward line _____

5. Person controlling the game _____

6. Can be awarded for rule-breaking _____

7. Adult games last for — _____

8. One who replaces an injured player _____

9. Some games are broadcast on — _____

10. Those who watch the match _____

11. A referee is helped by two — _____

12. The aim is to score as many — as possible _____

13. The Football League is made up of — _____

14. Games between countries are — _____

15. Players must obey the referee's — _____

7

1. find/fined	2. waist/waste	3. told/tolled
4. ewes/yews	5. sewn/sown	6. steak/stake
7. panes/pains	8. beach/beech	

1. She was — for careless driving   _____

2. It is wrong to — food   _____

3. A bell was — at the funeral   _____

4. Female sheep   _____

5. Patches were — on his jeans   _____

6. A pointed stick   _____

7. Two — of glass were broken   _____

8. Clay cliffs edged a sandy —   _____

Boys' Names

9. PHCHORSITER   13. ISEELL
10. RODHAL   12. CHARRID
11. ARHURT   14. TENSER   15. PHENEST

9. C   _____

10. H   _____

11. A   _____

12. R   _____

13. L   _____

14. E   _____

15. S   _____

Police

arrested   Alsatian   magistrate   policewomen
summons   sergeant   witnesses   juvenile court
beat   officer   detectives   personal radio
Criminal Investigation Department   emergency
handcuffs

1. Stopped and caught by the police   _____

2. Type of dog used by police   _____

3. Children are tried in a —   _____

4. Area patrolled by a policeman   _____

5. What does C.I.D. mean?   _____

6. Police working in plain clothes   _____

7. Name for women in the police   _____

8. Letter ordering one to appear at court   _____

9. Keeps constables in touch with the station   _____

10. A policeman is an — of the law   _____

11. Call the police in an —   _____

12. Man or woman who tries people   _____

13. Metal rings slipped on the wrists   _____

14. People who saw what happened   _____

15. Three stripes indicate the rank of —   _____

Weapons

catapult   rifle   boomerang   rapier

hand-grenade   crossbow   longbow

dagger   blowpipe   battle axe

1. _____   6. _____

2. _____   7. _____

3. _____   8. _____

4. _____   9. _____

5. _____   10. _____

Score

remember the 'e'	measurements	amusements	
	arrangements	excitement	advertisement

1. Entertainments   _____
2. The tennis finals caused great —   _____
3. She saw a job in an —   _____
4. Plans   _____
5. How long, how wide, etc.   _____

y	syllable	symbol	
	Olympic		crypt

6. Games held every four years   _____
7. Underground room beneath a church   _____
8. Part of a word   _____
9. ÷ is a — meaning divide   _____

Flowers	hyacinth	geranium	marigold	
	gladioli	daffodil	lavender	

10. - -r- -i- -   _____
11. - -a- -o- -   _____
12. -a-e-d- -   _____
13. -a- -o-i-   _____
14. - -a- -n- -   _____
15. -a- - -ol-   _____

Indoors

> patience   rehearsals   embroidery   discotheque
> cue   wrestling   gymnastics   budgerigars
> billiards   chess   badminton   high-fidelity
> whist   carpentry   philately

1. Judo and karate are forms of — _____

2. Kind of indoor tennis _____

3. Played on green table with 3 balls _____

4. Birds kept as pets _____

5. Long stick for billiards and snooker _____

6. Practice times for actors _____

7. Card game for one player _____

8. Card game for four players _____

9. Exercises often with bars, mats, etc. _____

10. Woodwork _____

11. Stamp-collecting _____

12. Place for dancing to records _____

13. Decorating with needle and thread _____

14. Hi-fi means — _____

15. Played on a board with 64 squares _____

Feminine { empress   tigress   manageress   waitress   goddess }

1. Manager   _____
2. God   _____
3. Emperor   _____
4. Waiter   _____
5. Tiger   _____

fore { forecourt   foretell   forefinger   foremost   forename }

6. To tell what is going to happen   _____
7. First name   _____
8. Area in front of a building   _____
9. First finger after the thumb   _____
10. In front of the others   _____

using 'ir' { irreversible   irreparable   irresponsible   irresistible   irreplaceable }

11. Cannot be replaced   _____
12. Cannot be reversed   _____
13. Not responsible   _____
14. Cannot be put right   _____
15. Cannot be resisted   _____

Large Cities

Mexico City	Peking	Moscow	Shanghai
Buenos Aires	Tokyo	London	New York
Bombay	Rio de Janeiro		

1. Capital city of China   _____

2. India's biggest city   _____

3. Capital city of Mexico   _____

4. In England and capital of U.K.   _____

5. Largest city in China   _____

6. In Japan and one of the world's largest cities   _____

7. Capital city of Russia   _____

8. Skyscraper city in U.S.A.   _____

9. In Brazil, S. America's biggest country   _____

10. On River Plate and capital of Argentina   _____

from Latin { afternoon   in the year of our Lord   that is   before noon   for example

11. A.D. (Anno Domini)   _____

12. a.m. (ante meridiem)   _____

13. p.m. (post meridiem)   _____

14. e.g. (exempli gratia)   _____

15. i.e. (id est)   _____

14

Dog Show

1. _____
2. _____
3. _____
4. _____
5. _____

6. _____
7. _____
8. _____
9. _____
10. _____

Score

15

> 1. rapped/wrapped   2. coarse/course
> 3. prayed/preyed   4. leek/leak   5. reins/reigns
> 6. died/dyed   7. heel/heal   8. isles/aisles

1. The stranger — twice on the door _____

2. — means rough _____

3. Her cat — on the sparrows _____

4. A vegetable like an onion _____

5. The jockey held the — loosely _____

6. The curtains were — a deep blue _____

7. A part of the foot _____

8. Paths between rows of seats _____

Girls' Names

> 9. TARGMEAR   12. ENRIE
> 11. RAYMOSER   14. NEVNOY
> 10. NELAGA   13. ILOSUE   15. MOINA

9. M _____

10. A _____

11. R _____

12. I _____

13. L _____

14. Y _____

15. N _____

16

Motoring

ignition   radiator   fuel gauge   carburettor
licence   chauffeur   servicing   automatic
exhaust   puncture   upholstery   dashboard
Rolls-Royce   speedometer   accelerator

1. Shows how much petrol one has _____

2. Pedal to increase speed _____

3. Famous British car firm _____

4. Pipe for waste gases _____

5. Key for starting the car _____

6. Name for the instrument panel _____

7. Hole in a tyre _____

8. Person employed to drive a car _____

9. Word meaning seat covers, etc. _____

10. Checking and repairing _____

11. Contains water for cooling the engine _____

12. It is illegal to drive without one _____

13. Self-changing gearboxes are — _____

14. Shows how fast the car is going _____

15. That part of the engine which mixes petrol vapour with air _____

acc {
    accomplice   account   accuse
        accompany   accurate
}

1. Statement of money in the bank _____

2. Blame _____

3. Go along with _____

4. Partner in crime _____

5. Exact _____

Surnames	Sutcliffe N.O.	Sykes J.	Whitfield V.
	Bennett A.D.	Sykes P.J.	Priestley R.S.
	McKenzie M.C.	Willoughby J.	
	Barraclough I.	Barraclough K.	

6. _____

7. _____

8. _____

9. In directories, filing cabinets, _____

10. etc. surnames have to be _____
    arranged in alphabetical order

11. for easy reference. Write out _____

12. this list in alphabetical order. _____

13. _____

14. _____

15. _____

add 'led' { quarrel   shovel   control
              panel travel shrivel cancel
                  pencil   fulfil   swivel }

1. Drawn with a pencil   _____

2. Directed   _____

3. Journeyed   _____

4. Disagreed fiercely   _____

5. The leaves had — in the
   hot sun   _____

6. It was an oak — room   _____

7. The coal was quickly — into
   a sack   _____

8. Turned round   _____

9. Crossed out   _____

10. Being a doctor — her ambition _____

longer
forms { mackintosh   linoleum   aeroplane
           revolutions   microphone }

11. lino   _____

12. mike   _____

13. mack (or mac)   _____

14. revs   _____

15. plane   _____

19

Headgear

deerstalker   beret   wig

cap   trilby   bearskin

boater   bonnet   turban   bowler

1. _____

2. _____

3. _____

4. _____

5. _____

6. _____

7. _____

8. _____

9. _____

10. _____

Score

History

Julius Caesar / Thomas Becket / Winston Churchill
Edmund Barton / William the Conqueror / Goliath
Oliver Cromwell / Francis Drake / Horatio Nelson
Hannibal / Napoleon / Marie Curie / Guy Fawkes
Christopher Columbus / Boadicea

1. He tried to blow up James I   _____

2. Was defeated at Waterloo   _____

3. Rebelled against the Romans   _____

4. English priest murdered in
   Canterbury Cathedral   _____

5. Victor at Battle of Hastings   _____

6. Crossed the Alps with elephants   _____

7. Defeated the French at
   Trafalgar   _____

8. English Prime Minister in the
   Second World War   _____

9. Crossed the Atlantic in the
   Santa Maria   _____

10. Against Charles I in English
    Civil War   _____

11. Famous woman scientist   _____

12. Led first Roman army to Britain   _____

13. First Englishman to sail around
    the world   _____

14. First Australian Prime Minister   _____

15. Giant slain by a shepherd boy   _____

Flying

Concorde supersonic air hostess Amy Johnson
propeller glider helicopters Graf Zeppelin
biplane parachute Hurricane monoplane
galley altimeter Wilbur and Orville Wright

1. Famous fighter plane   _____

2. Planes used in rescues   _____

3. Word meaning a plane with
one wing   _____

4. Word meaning two-winged plane _____

5. Famous German airship   _____

6. Name for an airliner's kitchen   _____

7. First woman to fly alone to
Australia   _____

8. Word meaning above speed of
sound   _____

9. American brothers who first
flew a plane with an engine   _____

10. A plane with no engine   _____

11. Tells pilot how high he is
flying   _____

12. British plane faster than sound   _____

13. Used when jumping from a plane _____

14. She looks after you on a plane   _____

15. Spinning blade which moves
some aircraft   _____

22

remember the 'e'	encouragement	retirement
	engagement	
	announcement	commencement

1. When normal work ceases   _____
2. Promise to be married   _____
3. Start   _____
4. The child was given every —   _____
5. An -- was made over the radio   _____

ette	serviette	laundrette	kitchenette
	cassette	roulette	

6. A small kitchen   _____
7. For washing clothes   _____
8. A gambling game   _____
9. Table-napkin   _____
10. Contains recorded programmes   _____

Flowers	anemone	carnation	polyanthus
	hollyhock	delphinium	

11. --l---n---   _____
12. -o----t---   _____
13. -ol---o--   _____
14. --e-o--   _____
15. ----at---   _____

Fashion

cosmetics	anorak	pinafore	bracelet	boutique
zip-fastener	shawl	hairstyle	pyjamas	jewellery
mackintosh	sweater	scarves	cardigan	millinery

1. Modern method of fastening clothes   _____

2. Kind of apron with low neck   _____

3. How one's hair is arranged   _____

4. Triangular garment worn round the shoulders   _____

5. Knitted woollen jacket   _____

6. Kind of jersey   _____

7. Jacket with hood for bad weather   _____

8. Jacket and trousers for sleeping in   _____

9. Rings, necklaces, precious stones   _____

10. Ornament for arm or wrist   _____

11. A raincoat   _____

12. Make-up, perfumes, etc.   _____

13. Shop selling fashionable clothes   _____

14. Department for hats   _____

15. Neckwear in cold weather   _____

Vehicles

motor cycle   hovercraft   Concorde   ambulance
articulated lorry   petrol-tanker   helicopter
bicycle   hot-air balloon   caravan

1. _____

2. _____

3. _____

4. _____

5. _____

6. _____

7. _____

8. _____

9. _____

10. _____

Score

superior	tremor	transistor	operator
bachelor	navigator	councillor	objector
inventor	orator	calculator	survivor
radiator	accelerator	refrigerator	

or

1. An unmarried man   _____

2. A fine speaker   _____

3. Control for increasing speed   _____

4. Member of a council   _____

5. One who protests   _____

6. Plots course of ship or plane   _____

7. One who escapes with his life   _____

8. Shaking of the earth   _____

9. Keeps food cool   _____

10. Thinks up new things   _____

11. To work it out he used a
    pocket —   _____

12. Part of a radio   _____

13. The radio — sent an S.O.S.
    signal   _____

14. Warms a room   _____

15. Higher or better   _____

*The acrostic might make you say 'Snakes alive!'

Wild Life

weasel   alligator   flamingoes   cheetahs   aviary
rabies   Australia   chimpanzee   giraffe   spoor
kiwi   albatross   rhinoceros   Safari Parks
zoology

1. Very fast leopard-like animals   _____

2. A large bird cage   _____

3. Has one or two horns on its nose   _____

4. Country of the kangaroo   _____

5. Largest seabird   _____

6. Zoos where animals are quite free   _____

7. Tall, pink wading birds   _____

8. Deadly disease from foxes, dogs, etc.   _____

9. The study of animal life   _____

10. The track of a wild animal   _____

11. Flesh-eating animal like a stoat   _____

12. Most intelligent ape   _____

13. New Zealand bird which cannot fly   _____

14. Tallest animal in the world   _____

15. Like a crocodile, but has a shorter head   _____

Hockey { receiving   penalties   shoulder
         defence
         bullying   opponents   international

1. Awarded when rules are broken

2. Players on the opposing side

3. Games between countries

4. Gaining possession of the ball

5. Game starts by two players —

6. Sticks must not be raised above the —

7. Main task of backs, halfbacks and goalkeepers

Tennis { deuce   rallies   fault   doubles   umpire
         serving   Wimbledon   volleying

8. Famous place for tennis in Britain

9. Sees that the rules are obeyed

10. If both players have forty points the score is —

11. Game is started by one player —

12. Hitting the ball before it bounces

13. Game played between two couples

14. Periods of play without a break

15. If the service goes into the net it is a —

Holidays

picturesque   yacht   excursion   tourist
caravanners   skiing   brochure   illuminations
temperature   cabaret   foreigner   arrangements
restaurant   accommodation   destination

1. Word meaning 'beautiful to look at' _____

2. Thin booklet describing a place _____

3. A person who travels for pleasure _____

4. Place for meals _____

5. How hot or cold it is _____

6. End of the journey _____

7. Ship with sails _____

8. Fairy lights _____

9. Special trip, often for a party _____

10. Entertainment with a meal _____

11. Those who holiday in caravans _____

12. Person from another country _____

13. One's plans _____

14. Travelling on skis _____

15. The hotels were full; there was no more — _____

Musical Instruments

harp   double-bass   violin
accordion   trombone   cymbals   tuba
kettledrum   French horn   saxophone

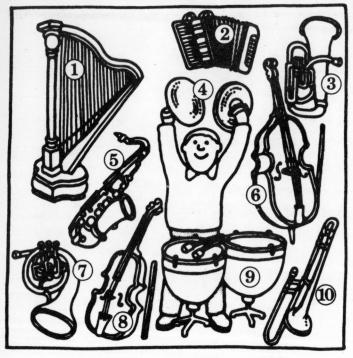

1. _____   6. _____
2. _____   7. _____
3. _____   8. _____
4. _____   9. _____
5. _____   10. _____

Score

Pop Music

guitars   popular   saxophone   accordion
lyric   ukelele   microphone   discotheque
Beatles   melodies   hysterical   vocalist
instrumentalist   pop festival   disc jockey

1. A name for the words of a song _____

2. World-famous pop group from Liverpool _____

3. Pop groups may play electric — _____

4. A wind instrument _____

5. Used by singers to increase sound _____

6. Name for one who plays an instrument _____

7. 'Pop' in pop music means — _____

8. Introduces programmes of records _____

9. A place for dancing to pop music _____

10. Instrument with keys like a piano _____

11. A small four-stringed instrument _____

12. Concert of music, often outdoors _____

13. Fans who show uncontrolled excitement are — _____

14. A word meaning singer _____

15. Tunes _____

exh ⎰ exhibition   exhume
     ⎱   exhausted   exhilarating

1. Very tired   _____

2. Dig out of the ground   _____

3. Exciting   _____

4. A display   _____

Surnames

Barrett M. Falkingham J. Richardson K. McNeil K.I.
Barrett N. Cartwright F. Matthews A.J. Whittaker L.S.
O'Brien H. McNaughton T. Beaumont C.

---

5.   _____

6.   _____

7.   _____

8.   _____

9.   Write out this list of names   _____
     in strict alphabetical order

10.   — as it would appear in a   _____
      telephone directory or

11.   filing system.   _____

12.   _____

13.   _____

14.   _____

15.   _____

Geography

Delhi	Maoris	Sphinx	stalactites	three-quarters
oasis	Cyprus	Vesuvius	Wellington	Scandinavia
linen	Rhine	Jupiter	physical	Niagara Falls

1. Native people of New Zealand   _____

2. Watering place in a desert   _____

3. Italian volcano   _____

4. Waterfalls between Lakes Erie and Ontario   _____

5. Maps showing hills, plains, rivers   _____

6. Cloth made from flax plant   _____

7. Fraction of earth covered by water   _____

8. Name for Norway, Sweden, Denmark   _____

9. Capital city of New Zealand   _____

10. Egyptian stone lion with human face   _____

11. Name of the largest planet   _____

12. Island in east Mediterranean   _____

13. Famous German river   _____

14. Capital city of India   _____

15. Icicle-shaped rocks hanging from roofs of caves   _____

which is it?

> 1. ball/bawl   2. vain/vane   3. medal/meddle
> 4. current/currant   5. through/threw
> 6. buries/berries   7. prophet/profit   8. souls/soles

1. Shout loudly   _____

2. Lightning struck the weather — _____

3. Interfere   _____

4. A swift — swept them away _____

5. Jim hurried — the turnstile _____

6. Our Alsatian always — its
   bones   _____

7. One who tells of future events _____

8. The — of his shoes were worn _____

longer
forms   { turpentine   veterinary surgeon   handkerchief   perambulator   mathematics   public house   omnibus

9. pram   _____

10. bus   _____

11. turps   _____

12. pub   _____

13. maths   _____

14. hanky   _____

15. vet   _____

Used

try-square   tape-measure   hammer

mallet   chisel   screwdriver

pliers   drill   spanner   plane

1. _____   6. _____

2. _____   7. _____

3. _____   8. _____

4. _____   9. _____

5. _____   10. _____

Score

Nature

pigeon   annuals   dormouse   pheasants   perennials
cuckoo   leveret   daffodil   dandelion   caterpillar
aphid   chrysalis kittiwake   mistletoe   mosquitoes

1. Plants living one year only _____

2. Insects breeding in stagnant
   water _____

3. Yellow flower from a bulb _____

4. Seabird with black wing-tips _____

5. Bird used in racing _____

6. Animal well-known for sleeping _____

7. Hatches from a butterfly's egg _____

8. Plant growing on apple and
   oak trees _____

9. Long-tailed birds reared for
   food _____

10. Lays eggs in another bird's
    nest _____

11. This splits and out comes a
    butterfly _____

12. Young hare _____

13. Greenfly _____

14. Wild flower with jagged leaves _____

15. Word meaning plants which
    grow year after year _____

Countries

1. RECEEG   2. DALGENN   3. KARMEND
4. YANKE   5. STARILUAA   6. LERAGIA
7. NATFISHAGAN   8. YONRAW   9. MEENY
10. HEARSTLENND   11. SNIPA   12. INAGIRE
13. SATURIA   14. GREATNANI   15. NOGALA

1. _____

2. _____

3. _____

4. _____

5. _____

6. _____

7. In these jumbled names the _____
   final letter of each name is
8. the starting letter of the _____
   next one
9. _____

10. _____

11. _____

12. _____

13. _____

14. _____

15. _____

add 'ly' { vertical   horizontal   fanatical
          unusual   gradual   theoretical

1. Slowly   _____
2. Strangely   _____
3. In a fanatical manner   _____
4. The rocket shot — into the sky   _____
5. The plane flew — across the
   airfield   _____
6. Opposite of practically   _____

Planets

7. PIJRUTE   8. RATSUN   9. TEENPUN

10. ARUNSU   11. HEART   12. NUVES

13. SARM   14. TOLUP   15. CRUMREY

7. J   _____
8. S   _____
9. N   _____
10. U   _____
11. E   _____
12. V   _____
13. M   _____
14. P   _____
15. M   _____

Acting

comedy   rehearsals   prompter   footlights
cue   properties   make-up   audience
scripts   producer   costumes   characters
Gilbert and Sullivan   moustache   playwright

1. A play to make us laugh _____

2. A writer of plays is known as a — _____

3. Person controlling the play _____

4. Tables, chairs, carpets, cups, etc. _____

5. Practice periods _____

6. Last word before next actor speaks _____

7. Grease paint, etc. for the actors _____

8. Word meaning the people in the play _____

9. Clothes the actors will wear _____

10. Copies of the play are known as – _____

11. Whispers forgotten lines to the actors _____

12. Those who watch the performance _____

13. Writers of famous operettas _____

14. Tim had to wear a false — _____

15. Lights across the front of the stage _____

Looked through

spectacles   microscope   magnifying glass
telescope   lorgnette   pince-nez   monocle
visor   periscope   binoculars

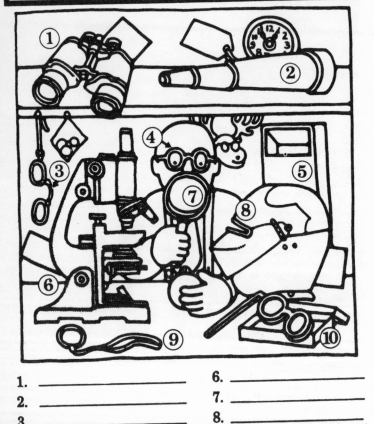

1. _____
2. _____
3. _____
4. _____
5. _____
6. _____
7. _____
8. _____
9. _____
10. _____

Score

40

our { parlour   journalist   armoured   journeys
      tambourine   courier   encourage
      coloured   courteous   neighbours }

1. Polite   _____
2. Travels   _____
3. Bullets came from an — car   _____
4. A writer of articles   _____
5. Sitting-room   _____
6. People who live near us   _____
7. Musical instrument   _____
8. Messenger, or guide for
   tourists   _____
9. — balloons were on sale   _____
10. To urge on   _____

dge { partridge   grudge   fidget
           cartridge   porridge }

11. Breakfast cereal of oats   _____
12. To give unwillingly   _____
13. She was told not to —   _____
14. A bird shot for food   _____
15. It is put into a rifle   _____

History

Socrates / Louis Blériot / Baden-Powell / Cleopatra
David Livingstone / Dr. Barnardo / William Wilberforce
Shakespeare / Abel Tasman / Joseph Stalin / Galileo
St. George / Alfred Tennyson / Lord Shaftesbury
Christopher Wren

1. English playwright from
   Stratford-on-Avon   _____

2. English M.P. who worked to
   abolish slavery   _____

3. Dutch explorer who discovered
   Tasmania   _____

4. Discovered the Victoria Falls   _____

5. Architect to St. Paul's
   Cathedral in London   _____

6. Leader of Russia for nearly
   30 years   _____

7. Famous Egyptian queen   _____

8. Started Boy Scouts/Girl Guides _____

9. Patron saint of England   _____

10. Greek thinker who drank poison _____

11. Famous English poet   _____

12. Began homes for homeless
    children   _____

13. First to fly the English Channel _____

14. Italian scientist who discovered
    the pendulum   _____

15. He improved conditions in
    English mines and factories _____

Dancing

ballerina   Bolshoi   castanets   hula-hula
orchestra   warriors   pirouette   discotheque
celebrate   quickstep   exercises   competition
Johann Strauss   square-dance   choreographer

1. Children danced around the
   maypole to – the start of summer _____

2. Chief female dancer in a ballet _____

3. In Hawaii – girls dance in
   grass skirts _____

4. A contest between dancers _____

5. A place for dancing to pop music _____

6. Famous Russian ballet school _____

7. A fast foxtrot _____

8. Clicking instruments used in
   Spanish dancing _____

9. War dances were performed by – _____

10. Practice movements _____

11. Famous Austrian writer of
    waltzes _____

12. Spin around on one foot _____

13. It provides the music _____

14. Arranges ballet steps and
    movements _____

15. American dance where a
    'caller' gives instructions. _____

43

add 'ed' { encounter uncover surrender murder stagger answer order thunder ladder remember

1. Gave up the fight _____

2. Commanded _____

3. Killed _____

4. Met _____

5. Past tense of remember _____

6. The drunken man — to his feet _____

7. Replied _____

8. Past tense of uncover _____

9. Snapped a thread in a stocking _____

10. After the lightning it — _____

* The acrostic gives something which is better done at six than sixty.

rr { stirred deferred interred occurred preferred

11. Past tense of prefer _____

12. Put off till later _____

13. Past tense of stir _____

14. Buried in the ground _____

15. Past tense of occur _____

Dress

toga   crinoline   armour   pyjamas

kimono   doublet and hose   poncho

cassock and surplice   overalls   jodhpurs

1. _____   6. _____

2. _____   7. _____

3. _____   8. _____

4. _____   9. _____

5. _____   10. _____

Score

Shopping

stationery   hosiery   guarantee   delicatessen
assistants   basement   waitresses   spendthrift
restaurant   boutique   escalator   detective
haberdashery   recommended   confectionery

1. For fashionable dresses, etc.   _____

2. Moving staircase   _____

3. Women who serve food at table   _____

4. A place for eating meals   _____

5. Person who watches for stealing   _____

6. Department for handkerchiefs, ribbons, etc.   _____

7. Writing materials   _____

8. Floor below ground level   _____

9. Socks, stockings, etc.   _____

10. Shop for sweets, cakes, etc.   _____

11. Person who wastes his money   _____

12. Sells cooked meats, sauces, etc.   _____

13. We take 10% off the manufacturer's — price   _____

14. Men and women who serve the customers   _____

15. A promise as to quality given with goods   _____

i before e —
except after c

shr--k	perc--ve	w--ld	dec--tful	misch--vous
rel--f	retr--ve	rec--ving	p--cemeal	f--ld glasses

1. Accepting   _____
2. Two-faced   _____
3. A bit at a time   _____
4. Naughty   _____
5. Yell   _____
6. Brandish or swing   _____
7. It was a — to pass the exam   _____
8. Binoculars   _____
9. To see   _____
10. To get back one's possessions   _____

Foreign Money { Franc   Dollar   Lira   Drachma   Peseta

11.	U.S.A. and Canada	_____
12.	France and Switzerland	_____
13.	Italy	_____
14.	Spain	_____
15.	Greece	_____

(Used in)

Surnames

Johnson D.S.   Clark T.   Taylor J.   Thompson R.P.
Stephenson S.   Clarke T.   Phillips J.R.   Shepherd A.B.
Campbell C.   Lloyd M.   McDonald I.   Nicholson P.J.
Williamson P.   Williamson O.   Stevenson W.W.

1.   _____

2.   _____

3.   _____

4.   _____

5.   _____

6. In a telephone directory or   _____

7. form register names must be   _____

8. in strict alphabetical order.   _____
   If you were writing a new

9. register, how would you   _____
   list these names?

10.   _____

11.   _____

12.   _____

13.   _____

14.   _____

15.   _____

Books

annual	authoress	bookworm	Shakespeare
recipe	catalogue	directory	dictionary
fiction	librarian	anthology	biography
Agatha Christie	William Caxton		encyclopedia

1. In charge of a library   _____
2. Book of words and meanings   _____
3. England's most famous playwright   _____
4. Book of telephone numbers   _____
5. Used for looking up facts   _____
6. Brought printing to England   _____
7. Word meaning invented stories   _____
8. Feminine of author   _____
9. One who is always reading   _____
10. Someone's life story   _____
11. Book which comes out each year   _____
12. Famous authoress of detective stories   _____
13. Lists of things to be sold   _____
14. Book of poems   _____
15. How to make the cake was in the — book   _____

Buildings

cooling towers   bungalow   cathedral
observatory   half-timbered house   mosque
oast-house   terraced houses   castle   greenhouse

1. _____   6. _____
2. _____   7. _____
3. _____   8. _____
4. _____   9. _____
5. _____   10. _____

Score

using 'un'

unnoticed   uneventful   unconscious   unscrupulous
unnatural   uncertain   unnecessary   unsatisfactory
uncomfortable   unsympathetic

1. Not necessary _____

2. Not noticed _____

3. Not natural _____

4. Not comfortable _____

5. Not satisfactory _____

6. Not sympathetic _____

7. Dull, not eventful _____

8. Unsure, not certain _____

9. Not conscious _____

10. Dishonest _____

Rivers { Thames   Mississippi   Murray   Amazon   Seine

11. The main river in Australia _____

12. Largest river in the world _____

13. London's river _____

14. Runs through Paris _____

15. The main river of the United States _____

Outdoors

capsize angling paraffin hazardous
archery compass rucksacks sanctuaries
dubbin rambling astronomy binoculars
trekking pot-holing Youth Hostels Association

1. Walking for pleasure   _____
2. Fishing with a hook and line   _____
3. Field-glasses   _____
4. Travelling by pony   _____
5. Y.H.A. means —   _____
6. Ramblers carry them on their backs   _____
7. Instrument for finding direction   _____
8. Shooting with bow and arrow   _____
9. Fuel used in some outdoor stoves   _____
10. Grease for waterproofing boots   _____
11. Study of sun, moon, stars, etc.   _____
12. Wrongly handled a canoe can   _____
13. Climbing without training can be —   _____
14. Exploring underground caves   _____
15. Protected areas for wild birds   _____

$\cancel{e}$ + ing $\begin{cases} \text{use} \quad \text{humiliate} \quad \text{seize} \quad \text{wrestle} \quad \text{separate} \\ \quad \text{argue} \\ \text{oblige} \quad \text{emphasise} \quad \text{rescue} \quad \text{evaporate} \end{cases}$

1. A type of fighting   _____
2. Debating, wrangling   _____
3. Saving a person from danger   _____
4. Stressing a point   _____
5. Shaming or disgracing   _____
6. Pleasing   _____
7. She was only — her brains   _____
8. Grabbing   _____
9. Drying up   _____
10. Dividing or parting   _____

*The acrostic gives the names of storage buildings

ss $\begin{cases} \text{successor} \quad \text{assassinate} \quad \text{reconnaissance} \\ \quad \text{narcissus} \quad \text{harass} \end{cases}$

11. Annoy again and again   _____
12. Murder   _____
13. Exploration of land to locate
    enemy, traps, etc.   _____
14. White flower grown from a bulb   _____
15. One who takes over from
    another   _____

You and Me?

diligent   faithful   dignified   insolent   melancholic
affluent   furtive   obstinate   generous   vivacious
cowardly   idle   dishonest   handsome   courageous

1. Good-looking   _____
2. Faint-hearted   _____
3. Sly   _____
4. Brave   _____
5. Stately   _____
6. Lazy   _____
7. Not mean   _____
8. Stubborn   _____
9. Sad   _____
10. Untruthful   _____
11. Cheeky   _____
12. Hardworking   _____
13. Loyal   _____
14. Rich   _____
15. Lively   _____

54

Shapes

circle square pentagon triangle octagon
hexagon rectangle quadrant ellipse segment

1. _____   6. _____
2. _____   7. _____
3. _____   8. _____
4. _____   9. _____
5. _____   10. _____

Score

ent {
permanent   impertinent
independent   benevolent   superintendent

1. Everlasting _____
2. Kind-hearted _____
3. Cheeky _____
4. Self-governing, free _____
5. Someone in charge _____

mm {
immediately   symmetrical   commencement
commentator   accommodation

6. Start _____
7. Evenly balanced _____
8. At once _____
9. Rooms, space, etc. in a building _____
10. One who describes an event _____

Tricky Ones {
inoculation   syllable
cenotaph   syllabus   teetotaller

11. 'Yes' is a word of one — _____
12. Scheme of work at school or college _____
13. One who does not have alcoholic drinks _____
14. Monument to the dead _____
15. Injection to protect against disease _____

Money

taxes   embezzler   miser   cashier

instalments   interest   pauper   receipt

millionaire   financial   cheque   bartering

currency   bankrupt   Building Societies

1. A very rich person   _____

2. They lend money to buy houses   _____

3. Money taken by the government   _____

4. Word meaning regular payments   _____

5. Person in charge of a firm's cash   _____

6. One who hoards every penny   _____

7. Word meaning exchanging goods   _____

8. Piece of paper sent instead of cash   _____

9. Unable to pay what is owed   _____

10. Money is the main topic in — papers   _____

11. The money that is used in a country   _____

12. Takes money which is not his own   _____

13. Money charged for a loan   _____

14. A very poor person   _____

15. Paper stating money has been received.   _____

Nursing

stethoscope / Switzerland / radiographer / surgeon
State Registered Nurse / contagious / anaesthetic
antiseptic / Florence Nightingale / thermometer
tourniquet / examinations / hypodermic syringes
pulse / theatre

1. Used by nurses to give injections _____

2. What does S.R.N. mean? _____

3. Chicken-pox is infectious and — _____

4. Used to take temperature _____

5. A person who performs
   operations _____

6. What is the operating room
   called? _____

7. Nurses must study for — _____

8. Listening instrument used by
   doctors _____

9. Person who X-rays the patient _____

10. Given so that no pain is felt _____

11. Regarded as founder of modern
    nursing _____

12. The Red Cross Society began in _____

13. Nurses hold the wrist to time
    the — _____

14. Stops bleeding by applying
    pressure _____

15. Something which kills germs _____

Cooking

recipes   preserves   mayonnaise   mackerel

coconut   beverages   sandwiches   meringue

garnish   filleting   seasoning   Worcester

ingredients   omelette   simmering

(or omelet)

1. Striped fish caught in the Atlantic   _____

2. Taking out the bones   _____

3. A word meaning drinks   _____

4. To keep something just bubbling   _____

5. Dried nut used in cooking   _____

6. A sauce named after a city   _____

7. Slices of bread and butter with a filling   _____

8. Instructions how to make cakes, etc.   _____

9. A dressing used with salads   _____

10. Those things which go into the mixture   _____

11. Eggs whipped, fried and folded   _____

12. Name for jams, marmalade, etc.   _____

13. Word meaning to decorate food   _____

14. Salt and pepper   _____

15. Egg-white and sugar mixture   _____

Apparatus

funnel   conical flask   Bunsen burner
test-tube   tripod   thistle funnel
balance   beaker   retort   burette

1. _____   6. _____
2. _____   7. _____
3. _____   8. _____
4. _____   9. _____
5. _____   10. _____

Score

Geography {
peninsula   fiord   Czechoslovakia
    Sicily   glacier   London
Hungary   Aborigines strait   plateau
}

1. Country whose capital is Budapest _____

2. Dark-skinned natives of Australia _____

3. Stretch of high level ground _____

4. Narrow leg of land jutting into sea _____

5. River of ice _____

6. Largest island in Mediterranean _____

7. Capital city of England _____

8. Narrow steep-sided inlet in coast _____

9. Country whose capital is Prague _____

10. A narrow strip of water _____

longer forms {
representatives   influenza   recapitulate
    memorandum   poliomyelitis
}

11. memo _____

12. polio _____

13. reps _____

14. recap _____

15. flu _____

proteins   feint   heiress   sleight-of-hand
sovereign   freight
forfeit   Fahrenheit   Frankenstein   Geiger counter

1. Scale on a thermometer _____

2. Female who will inherit property _____

3. Used when checking for radioactivity _____

4. Lines on this paper are very — _____

5. Gold coin or ruler of a country _____

6. Meat, fish, eggs are rich in — _____

7. Name for goods being transported _____

8. Quickness of a conjurer _____

9. Give up something _____

10. Monster in a famous story _____

exc   exception   exceeding   excess
       excise   excerpts

11. The driver was fined for — the speed limit _____

12. Extracts from books, films, etc. _____

13. Everyone went with the — of Margaret _____

14. Too much of something _____

15. Name for a tax on some goods _____

History

Mohammed / Napoleon Bonaparte / Edith Cavell / Aesop
Josiah Wedgwood / Augustine / Leonardo da Vinci
Mahatma Gandhi / Beethoven / Roald Amundsen
Rembrandt / Hans Andersen / Daniel Defoe / Marconi
Thomas Edison

1. Writer of famous fables _____

2. First archbishop of Canterbury
   in England _____

3. First explorer to reach South
   Pole _____

4. Italian scientist who developed
   wireless _____

5. Famous Dutch painter _____

6. English nurse executed in 1915 _____

7. Wrote 'Robinson Crusoe' _____

8. Painted the 'Mona Lisa' _____

9. Famous German composer _____

10. Famous Indian who taught
    non-violence _____

11. Writer of famous fairy tales _____

12. Founder of the Moslem religion _____

13. Famous English potter _____

14. Defeated at Battle of
    Waterloo _____

15. Invented gramophone and
    electric light bulb _____

(1)
1. reflector
2. mudguard
3. pneumatic
4. puncture
5. enamel
6. bicycle
7. tricycle
8. tyre-lever
9. lubricate
10. efficient
11. accidents
12. tandem
13. dynamo
14. milometer
15. maintenance

(2)
1. ceiling
2. believe
3. friend
4. thieves
5. patient
6. shield
7. piece
8. niece
9. deceive
10. receive
11. fitted
12. trotted
13. knitted
14. plotted
15. batted

(3)
1. sturdily
2. ordinarily
3. merrily
4. easily
5. readily
6. sleepily
7. angrily
8. unhappily
9. luckily
10. tidily
11. Australia
12. Greenland
13. New Guinea
14. Borneo
15. Malagasy
    Republic

(4)
1. detergent
2. caddy
3. saucepan
4. refrigerator
5. sieve
6. polythene
7. cupboards
8. casserole
9. ladle
10. scissors
11. greaseproof
12. percolator
13. dessert
14. drawers
15. serrated

(5)
1. factory
2. pyramid
3. hangar
4. railway
   station
5. palace
6. skyscraper
7. theatre
8. detached
   house
9. thatched
   cottage
10. semi-
    detached
    house

(6)
1. millimetre
2. metre
3. kilogram
4. centimetre
5. kilometre
6. seize
7. foreigner
8. leisure
9. Sheila
10. Neil
11. Eiffel Tower
12. gasometer
13. altimeter
14. thermometer
15. barometer

(7)

1. professional
2. amateur
3. Football Association
4. centre-forward
5. referee
6. penalty kick
7. ninety minutes
8. substitute
9. television
10. spectators
11. linesmen
12. goals
13. divisions
14. international
15. decisions

(8)

1. fined
2. waste
3. tolled
4. ewes
5. sewn
6. stake
7. panes
8. beach
9. Christopher
10. Harold
11. Arthur
12. Richard
13. Leslie
14. Ernest
15. Stephen

(9)

1. arrested
2. Alsatian
3. juvenile court
4. beat
5. Criminal Investigation Department
6. detectives
7. policewomen
8. summons
9. personal radio
10. officer
11. emergency
12. magistrate
13. handcuffs
14. witnesses
15. sergeant

(10)

1. rifle
2. longbow
3. battle axe
4. blowpipe
5. rapier
6. catapult
7. dagger
8. crossbow
9. boomerang
10. hand-grenade

(11)

1. amusements
2. excitement
3. advertisement
4. arrangements
5. measurements
6. Olympic
7. crypt
8. syllable
9. symbol
10. geranium
11. gladioli
12. lavender
13. daffodil
14. hyacinth
15. marigold

(12)

1. wrestling
2. badminton
3. billiards
4. budgerigars
5. cue
6. rehearsals
7. patience
8. whist
9. gymnastics
10. carpentry
11. philately
12. discotheque
13. embroidery
14. high-fidelity
15. chess

(13)

1. manageress
2. goddess
3. empress
4. waitress
5. tigress
6. foretell
7. forename
8. forecourt
9. forefinger
10. foremost
11. irreplaceable
12. irreversible
13. irresponsible
14. irreparable
15. irresistible

(14)

1. Peking
2. Bombay
3. Mexico City
4. London
5. Shanghai
6. Tokyo
7. Moscow
8. New York
9. Rio de Janeiro
10. Buenos Aires
11. in the year of our Lord
12. before noon
13. afternoon
14. for example
15. that is

(15)

1. dachshund
2. Labrador
3. bulldog
4. corgi
5. poodle
6. spaniel
7. Dalmatian
8. Pekinese
9. fox-terrier
10. collie

(16)

1. rapped
2. coarse
3. preyed
4. leek
5. reins
6. dyed
7. heel
8. aisles
9. Margaret
10. Angela
11. Rosemary
12. Irene
13. Louise
14. Yvonne
15. Naomi

(17)

1. fuel gauge
2. accelerator
3. Rolls-Royce
4. exhaust
5. ignition
6. dashboard
7. puncture
8. chauffeur
9. upholstery
10. servicing
11. radiator
12. licence
13. automatic
14. speedometer
15. carburettor

(18)

1. account
2. accuse
3. accompany
4. accomplice
5. accurate
6. Barraclough I.
7. Barraclough K.
8. Bennett A.D.
9. McKenzie M.C.
10. Priestley R.S.
11. Sutcliffe N.O.
12. Sykes J.
13. Sykes P.J.
14. Whitfield V.
15. Willoughby J.

(19)
1. pencilled
2. controlled
3. travelled
4. quarrelled
5. shrivelled
6. panelled
7. shovelled
8. swivelled
9. cancelled
10. fulfilled
11. linoleum
12. microphone
13. mackintosh
14. revolutions
15. aeroplane

(20)
1. boater
2. bonnet
3. trilby
4. bowler
5. bearskin
6. beret
7. wig
8. turban
9. deerstalker
10. cap

(21)
1. Guy Fawkes
2. Napoleon
3. Boadicea
4. Thomas Becket
5. William the Conqueror
6. Hannibal
7. Horatio Nelson
8. Winston Churchill
9. Christopher Columbus
10. Oliver Cromwell
11. Marie Curie
12. Julius Caesar
13. Francis Drake
14. Edmund Barton
15. Goliath

(22)
1. Hurricane
2. helicopters
3. monoplane
4. biplane
5. Graf Zeppelin
6. galley
7. Amy Johnson
8. supersonic
9. Wilbur and Orville Wright
10. glider
11. altimeter
12. Concorde
13. parachute
14. air hostess
15. propeller

(23)
1. retirement
2. engagement
3. commencement
4. encouragement
5. announcement
6. kitchenette
7. laundrette
8. roulette
9. serviette
10. cassette
11. delphinium
12. polyanthus
13. hollyhock
14. anemone
15. carnation

(24)
1. zip-fastener
2. pinafore
3. hairstyle
4. shawl
5. cardigan
6. sweater
7. anorak
8. pyjamas
9. jewellery
10. bracelet
11. mackintosh
12. cosmetics
13. boutique
14. millinery
15. scarves

(25)
1. Concorde
2. helicopter
3. hot-air balloon
4. hovercraft
5. caravan
6. bicycle
7. ambulance
8. articulated lorry
9. motor cycle
10. petrol tanker

(26)
1. bachelor
2. orator
3. accelerator
4. councillor
5. objector
6. navigator
7. survivor
8. tremor
9. refrigerator
10. inventor
11. calculator
12. transistor
13. operator
14. radiator
15. superior

(27)
1. cheetahs
2. aviary
3. rhinoceros
4. Australia
5. albatross
6. Safari Parks
7. flamingoes
8. rabies
9. zoology
10. spoor
11. weasel
12. chimpanzee
13. kiwi
14. giraffe
15. alligator

(28)
1. penalties
2. opponents
3. international
4. receiving
5. bullying
6. shoulder
7. defence
8. Wimbledon
9. umpire
10. deuce
11. serving
12. volleying
13. doubles
14. rallies
15. fault

(29)
1. picturesque
2. brochure
3. tourist
4. restaurant
5. temperature
6. destination
7. yacht
8. illuminations
9. excursion
10. cabaret
11. caravanners
12. foreigner
13. arrangements
14. skiing
15. accommodation

(30)
1. harp
2. accordion
3. tuba
4. cymbals
5. saxophone
6. double bass
7. French horn
8. violin
9. kettledrum
10. trombone

(31)	(32)	(33)
1. lyric	1. exhausted	1. Maoris
2. Beatles	2. exhume	2. oasis
3. guitars	3. exhilarating	3. Vesuvius
4. saxophone	4. exhibition	4. Niagara Falls
5. microphone	5. Barrett M.	5. physical
6. instrumentalist	6. Barrett N.	6. linen
7. popular	7. Beaumont C.	7. three-quarters
8. disc jockey	8. Cartwright F.	8. Scandinavia
9. discotheque	9. Falkingham J.	9. Wellington
10. accordion	10. Matthews A.J.	10. Sphinx
11. ukelele	11. McNaughton T.	11. Jupiter
12. pop festival	12. McNeil K.I.	12. Cyprus
13. hysterical	13. O'Brien H.	13. Rhine
14. vocalist	14. Richardson K.	14. Delhi
15. melodies	15. Whittaker L.S.	15. stalactites

(34)	(35)	(36)
1. bawl	1. drill	1. annuals
2. vane	2. try-square	2. mosquitoes
3. meddle	3. screwdriver	3. daffodil
4. current	4. spanner	4. kittiwake
5. through	5. tape-measure	5. pigeon
6. buries	6. hammer	6. dormouse
7. prophet	7. mallet	7. caterpillar
8. soles	8. chisel	8. mistletoe
9. perambulator	9. pliers	9. pheasants
10. omnibus	10. plane	10. cuckoo
11. turpentine		11. chrysalis
12. public house		12. leveret
13. mathematics		13. aphid
14. handkerchief		14. dandelion
15. veterinary surgeon		15. perennials

(37)
1. Greece
2. England
3. Denmark
4. Kenya
5. Australia
6. Algeria
7. Afghanistan
8. Norway
9. Yemen
10. Netherlands
11. Spain
12. Nigeria
13. Austria
14. Argentina
15. Angola

(38)
1. gradually
2. unusually
3. fanatically
4. vertically
5. horizontally
6. theoretically
7. Jupiter
8. Saturn
9. Neptune
10. Uranus
11. Earth
12. Venus
13. Mars
14. Pluto
15. Mercury

(39)
1. comedy
2. playwright
3. producer
4. properties
5. rehearsals
6. cue
7. make-up
8. characters
9. costumes
10. scripts
11. prompter
12. audience
13. Gilbert and Sullivan
14. moustache
15. footlights

(40)
1. binoculars
2. telescope
3. pince-nez
4. spectacles
5. periscope
6. microscope
7. magnifying glass
8. visor
9. monocle
10. lorgnette

(41)
1. courteous
2. journeys
3. armoured
4. journalist
5. parlour
6. neighbours
7. tambourine
8. courier
9. coloured
10. encourage
11. porridge
12. grudge
13. fidget
14. partridge
15. cartridge

(42)
1. Shakespeare
2. William Wilberforce
3. Abel Tasman
4. David Livingstone
5. Christopher Wren
6. Joseph Stalin
7. Cleopatra
8. Baden-Powell
9. St. George
10. Socrates
11. Alfred Tennyson
12. Dr. Barnardo
13. Louis Blériot
14. Galileo
15. Lord Shaftesbury

(43)
1. celebrate
2. ballerina
3. hula-hula
4. competition
5. discotheque
6. Bolshoi
7. quickstep
8. castanets
9. warriors
10. excercises
11. Johann Strauss
12. pirouette
13. orchestra
14. choreographer
15. square-dance

(44)
1. surrendered
2. ordered
3. murdered
4. encountered
5. remembered
6. staggered
7. answered
8. uncovered
9. laddered
10. thundered
11. preferred
12. deferred
13. stirred
14. interred
15. occurred

(45)
1. jodhpurs
2. overalls
3. cassock and surplice
4. toga
5. crinoline
6. armour
7. doublet and hose
8. pyjamas
9. kimono
10. poncho

(46)
1. boutique
2. escalator
3. waitresses
4. restaurant
5. detective
6. haberdashery
7. stationery
8. basement
9. hosiery
10. confectionery
11. spendthrift
12. delicatessen
13. recommended
14. assistants
15. guarantee

(47)
1. receiving
2. deceitful
3. piecemeal
4. mischievous
5. shriek
6. wield
7. relief
8. field glasses
9. perceive
10. retrieve
11. Dollar
12. Franc
13. Lira
14. Peseta
15. Drachma

(48)
1. Campbell C.
2. Clark T.
3. Clarke T.
4. Johnson D.S.
5. Lloyd M.
6. McDonald I
7. Nicholson P.J.
8. Phillips J.R.
9. Shepherd A.B.
10. Stephenson S.
11. Stevenson W.W.
12. Taylor J.
13. Thompson R.P.
14. Williamson O.
15. Williamson P.

(49)
1. librarian
2. dictionary
3. Shakespeare
4. directory
5. encyclopedia
6. William Caxton
7. fiction
8. authoress
9. bookworm
10. biography
11. annual
12. Agatha Christie
13. catalogue
14. anthology
15. recipe

(50)
1. cooling towers
2. observatory
3. oast-house
4. castle
5. greenhouse
6. cathedral
7. terraced-house
8. half-timbered house
9. mosque
10. bungalow

(51)
1. unnecessary
2. unnoticed
3. unnatural
4. uncomfortable
5. unsatisfactory
6. unsympathetic
7. uneventful
8. uncertain
9. unconscious
10. unscrupulous
11. Murray
12. Amazon
13. Thames
14. Seine
15. Mississippi

(52)
1. rambling
2. angling
3. binoculars
4. trekking
5. Youth Hostels Association
6. rucksacks
7. compass
8. archery
9. paraffin
10. dubbin
11. astronomy
12. capsize
13. hazardous
14. pot-holing
15. sanctuaries

(53)
1. wrestling
2. arguing
3. rescuing
4. emphasising
5. humiliating
6. obliging
7. using
8. seizing
9. evaporating
10. separating
11. harass
12. assassinate
13. reconnaissance
14. narcissus
15. successor

(54)
1. handsome
2. cowardly
3. furtive
4. courageous
5. dignified
6. idle
7. generous
8. obstinate
9. melancholy
10. dishonest
11. insolent
12. diligent
13. faithful
14. affluent
15. vivacious

(55)
1. octagon
2. hexagon
3. quadrant
4. rectangle
5. circle
6. segment
7. square
8. triangle
9. ellipse
10. pentagon

(56)
1. permanent
2. benevolent
3. impertinent
4. independent
5. superintendent
6. commencement
7. symmetrical
8. immediately
9. accommodation
10. commentator
11. syllable
12. syllabus
13. teetotaller
14. cenotaph
15. inoculation

(57)
1. millionaire
2. Building Societies
3. taxes
4. instalments
5. cashier
6. miser
7. bartering
8. cheque
9. bankrupt
10. financial
11. currency
12. embezzler
13. interest
14. pauper
15. receipt

(58)
1. hypodermic syringes
2. State Registered Nurse
3. contagious
4. thermometer
5. surgeon
6. theatre
7. examinations
8. stethoscope
9. radiographer
10. anaesthetic
11. Florence Nightingale
12. Switzerland
13. pulse
14. tourniquet
15. antiseptic

(59)
1. mackerel
2. filleting
3. beverages
4. simmering
5. coconut
6. Worcester
7. sandwiches
8. recipes
9. mayonnaise
10. ingredients
11. omelette (or omelet)
12. preserves
13. garnish
14. seasoning
15. meringue

(60)
1. burette
2. funnel
3. retort
4. balance
5. tripod
6. Bunsen burner
7. conical flask
8. beaker
9. thistle funnel
10. test-tube

(61)	(62)	(63)
1. Hungary	1. Fahrenheit	1. Aesop
2. Aborigines	2. heiress	2. Augustine
3. plateau	3. Geiger counter	3. Roald Amundsen
4. peninsula	4. feint	4. Marconi
5. glacier	5. sovereign	5. Rembrandt
6. Sicily	6. proteins	6. Edith Cavell
7. London	7. freight	7. Daniel Defoe
8. fiord	8. sleight-of-hand	8. Leonardo da Vinci
9. Czechoslovakia	9. forfeit	9. Beethoven
10. strait	10. Frankenstein	10. Mahatma Gandhi
11. memorandum	11. exceeding	11. Hans Andersen
12. poliomyelitis	12. excerpts	12. Mohammed
13. representatives	13. exception	13. Josiah Wedgwood
14. recapitulate	14. excess	14. Napoleon Bonaparte
15. influenza	15. excise	15. Thomas Edison